DESIGN**AMERICA**
presents

modern
FARMHOUSE

OVER 125 POPULAR HOME PLANS

DESIGNAMERICA

Current Printing (last digit)
10 9 8 7 6 5 4 3 2

Design America™ presents Modern Farmhouse - Over 125 Popular Home Plans
ISBN-13: 978-1-58678-011-1

DESIGN AMERICA, INC.™
designamerica.com

The homes on the cover are: Top, Plan #904-076D-0220 on page 76; Plan #051D-0960 on page 40; Plan #904-152D-0049 on page 96; Bottom: Plan #904-011S-0189; All plans available for purchase at houseplansandmore.com.

Home featured on page 1: Plan #904-101D-0080 on page 36.

CONTENTS

Top to bottom: Plan #904-101D-0050 on page 92; Plan #904-152D-0049 on page 96; Plan #904-101D-0056, on page 10; Plan #904-051D-0977 on page 97; Plan #904-028D-0099 on page 82; Plan #904-101D-0087 on page 83.

what's the right **PLAN** for you?

Choosing a house design is exciting, but can be a difficult task. Many factors play a role in what home plan is best for you and your family. To help you get started, we have pinpointed some of the major factors to consider when searching for your dream home. Take the time to evaluate your family's needs and you will have an easier time sorting through all of the house designs offered in this book.

BUDGET is the first thing to consider. Many items take part in this budget, from ordering the blueprints to the last door-knob purchased. When you find the perfect house plan, visit houseplansandmore.com and get a cost-to-build estimate to ensure that the finished home will be within your cost range. A cost-to-build report is a detailed summary that gives you the total cost to build a specific home in the zip code where you're planning to build. It is interactive, allowing you to adjust labor and material costs, and it's created on demand when ordered so all pricing is up-to-date. This valuable tool will help you know how much your dream home will cost before you buy plans (see page 106 for more information).

MAKE A LIST
Experts in the field suggest that the best way to determine your needs is to begin by listing everything you like or dislike about your current home.

FAMILY LIFESTYLE After your budget is deciphered, you need to assess you and your family's lifestyle needs. Think about the stage of life you are in now, and what stages you will be going through in the future. Ask yourself questions to figure out how much room you need now and if you will need room for expansion. Are you married? Do you have children? How many children do you plan on having? Are you an empty-nester? How long do you plan to live in this home?

Incorporate into your planning any frequent guests you may have including elderly parents, grandchildren or adult children who may live with you.

Does your family entertain a lot? If so, think about the rooms you will need to do so. Will you need both formal and informal spaces? Do you need a gourmet kitchen? Do you need a game room and/or a wet bar?

FLOOR PLAN LAYOUTS When looking through these home plans, imagine yourself walking through the house. Consider the flow from the entry to the living, sleeping and gathering areas. Does the layout ensure privacy for the master bedroom? Does the garage enter near the kitchen for easy unloading? Does the placement of the windows provide enough privacy from any neighboring properties? Do you plan on using furniture you already have? Will this furniture fit in the appropriate rooms? When you find a plan you want to purchase, be sure to picture yourself actually living in it.

EXTERIOR SPACES With many different Modern Farmhouse designs throughout this book, flip through and find which home appeals to you the most and think about the neighborhood in which you plan to build. Also, think about how the house will fit on your site. Picture the landscaping you want to add to the lot. Using your imagination is key when choosing a home plan.

Choosing a house design can be an intimidating experience. Asking yourself these questions before you get started on the search will help you through the process. With our large selection of sizes and styles, we are certain you will find your dream home in this book.

10 steps to BUILDING your dream home

1 TALK TO A LENDER

If you plan to obtain a loan in order to build your new home, then it's best to find out first how much you can get approved for before selecting a home design. Knowing the financial information before you start looking for land or a home will keep you from selecting something out of your budget and turning a great experience into a major disappointment. Financing the home you plan to build is somewhat different than financing the purchase of an existing house. You're going to need thousands of dollars for land, labor, and materials. Chances are, you're going to have to borrow most of it. Therefore, you will probably need to obtain a construction loan. This is a short-term loan to pay for building your house. When the house is completed, the loan is paid off in full, usually out of the proceeds from your long-term mortgage loan.

2 DETERMINE NEEDS

Selecting the right home plan for your needs and lifestyle requires a lot of thought. Your new home is an investment, so you should consider not only your current needs, but also your future requirements. Versatility and the potential for converting certain areas to other uses could be an important factor later on. So, although a home office may seem unnecessary now, in years to come, the idea may seem ideal. Home plans that include flex spaces or bonus rooms can really adapt to your needs in the future.

3 CHOOSE A HOMESITE

The site for your new home will have a definite impact on the design you select. It's a good idea to select a home that will complement your site. This will save you time and money when building. Or, you can then modify a design to specifically accommodate your site. However, it will most likely make your home construction more costly than selecting a home plan suited for your lot right from the start. For example, if your land slopes, a walk-out basement works perfectly. If it's wooded, or has a lake in the back, an atrium ranch home is a perfect style to take advantage of surrounding backyard views.

SOME IMPORTANT CRITERIA TO CONSIDER WHEN SELECTING A HOMESITE:

- Improvements will have to be made including utilities, walks and driveways
- Convenience of the lot to work, school, shops, etc.
- Zoning requirements and property tax amounts
- Soil conditions at your future site
- Make sure the person or firm that sells you the land owns it free and clear

4 SELECT A HOME DESIGN

We've chosen the "best of the best" new Modern Farmhouse home plans found at houseplansandmore.com to be featured in this book. With over 18,000 home plans from the best architects and designers across the country, this book includes the best variety of styles and sizes to suit the needs and tastes of a broad spectrum of homeowners.

5 GET THE COST TO BUILD

If you feel you have found "the" home, then before taking the step of purchasing house plans, order an estimated cost-to-build report for the exact zip code where you plan to build. Requesting this custom cost report created specifically for you will help educate you on all costs asso-

ciated with building your new home. Simply order this report and gain knowledge of the material and labor cost associated with the home you love. Not only does the report allow you to choose the quality of the materials, you can also select options in every aspect of the project from lot condition to contractor fees. This report will allow you to successfully manage your construction budget in all areas, clearly see where the majority of the costs lie, and save you money from start to finish.

A COST TO BUILD REPORT WILL DETERMINE THE OVERALL COST OF YOUR NEW HOME INCLUDING THESE 5 MAJOR EXPENSE CATEGORIES:

- Land
- Foundation
- Materials
- General Contractor's fee - Some rules-of-thumb that you may find useful are: (a) the total labor cost will generally run a little higher than your total material cost, but it's not unusual for a builder or general contractor to charge 15-20% of the combined cost for managing the overall project.
- Site improvements - don't forget to add in the cost of your site improvements such as utilities, driveway, sidewalks, landscaping, etc.

6 HIRE A CONTRACTOR

If you're inexperienced in construction, you'll probably want to hire a general contractor to manage the project. If you do not know a reputable general contractor, begin your search by contacting your local Home Builders Association to get references. Many states require building contractors to be licensed. If this is the case in your state, its licensing board is another referral source. Finding a reputable, quality-minded contractor is a key factor in ensuring that your new home is well constructed and is finished on time and within budget. It can be a smart decision to discuss the plan you like with your builder prior to ordering plans. They can guide you into choosing the right type of plan package option especially if you intend on doing some customizing to the design.

7 CUSTOMIZING

Sometimes your general contractor may want to be the one who makes the modifications you want to the home you've selected. But, sometimes they want to receive the plans ready to build. That is why we offer home plan modification services. Please see page 109 for specific information on the customizing process and how to get a free quote on the changes you want to make to a home before you buy the plans.

8 ORDER HOME PLANS

If you've found the home and are ready to order blueprints, we recommend ordering the PDF file format, which offers the most flexibility. A PDF file format will be emailed to you when you order, and it includes a copyright release from the designer, meaning you have the legal right to make changes to the plan if necessary as well as print out as many copies of the plan as you need for building the home one-time. You will be happy to have your blueprints saved electronically so they can easily be shared with your contractor, subcontractors, lender and local building officials. We do, however, offer several different types of plan package depending on your needs, so please refer to page 107 for all plan options available and choose the best one for your particular situation.

Another helpful component in the building process that is available for many of the house plans in this book is a material list. A material list includes not only a detailed list of materials, but it also indicates where various cuts of lumber and other building components are to be used. This will save your general contractor significant time and money since they won't have to create this list before building begins. If a material list is available for a home, it is indicated in the plan data box on the specific plan page in this book.

9 ORDER MATERIALS

You can order materials yourself, or have your contractor do it. Nevertheless, in order to thoroughly enjoy your new home you will want to personally select many of the materials that go into its construction. Today, home improvement stores offer a wide variety of quality building products. Only you can decide what specific types of windows, cabinets, bath fixtures, etc. will make your new home yours. Spend time early on in the construction process looking at the materials and products available.

10 MOVE IN

With careful planning and organization, your new home will be built on schedule and ready for your move-in date. Be sure to have all of your important documents in place for the closing of your new home and then you'll be ready to move in and start living your dream.

Browse the pages of *Design America™ presents Modern Farmhouse* and discover over 125 Modern Farmhouse designs in a variety of sizes to suit many tastes and budgets. There is a Modern Farmhouse design for everyone, and with all of the amenities and features homeowners are looking for in a new home today. Start your search for the perfect Modern Farmhouse right now!

Top, left: Plan #904-076D-0220 on page 76; top, right: Plan #904-028D-0097 on page 16; bottom, left: Plan #904-101D-0088 on page 93; bottom, right: Plan #904-155D-0070, on page 37.

PLAN #904-101D-0093

Dimensions:	76'9" W x 70'6" D
Heated Sq. Ft.:	2,615
Bonus Sq. Ft.:	2,274
Bedrooms: 2	Bathrooms: 2½
Exterior Walls:	2" x 6"
Foundation:	Basement

See index on page 104 for more information

FEATURES

- The great room and kitchen combine to create the central gathering place
- Tucked away in the rear is a cozy hearth room for added peace and quiet
- Decorative columns grace the formal dining area
- What an impressive master bedroom with covered deck access, a large walk-in closet and bath with corner garden tub, shower and double bowl vanity
- The optional lower level has an additional 2,274 square feet of living area and features a home theater, Lego® room, living room, billiards, bar, mechanical room, two bedrooms and two and a half baths
- 3-car front entry garage

Images provided by designer/architect

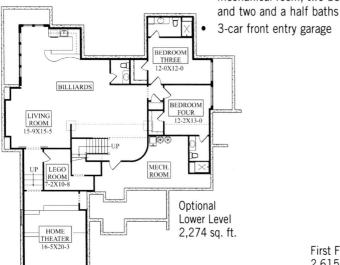

Optional
Lower Level
2,274 sq. ft.

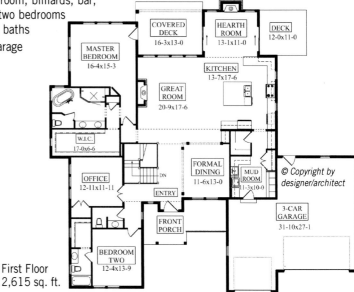

© Copyright by designer/architect

First Floor
2,615 sq. ft.

CALL 1-800-373-2646   **ONLINE** houseplansandmore.com

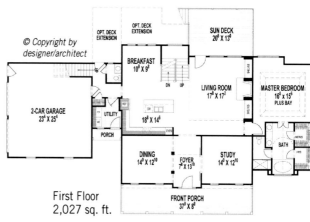

Second Floor
1,263 sq. ft.

PLAN #904-052D-0170

Dimensions:	88' W x 49' D
Heated Sq. Ft.:	3,290
Bonus Sq. Ft.:	2,315
Bedrooms: 4	Bathrooms: 3½
Foundation:	Walk-out basement

See index on page 104 for more information

Images provided by designer/architect

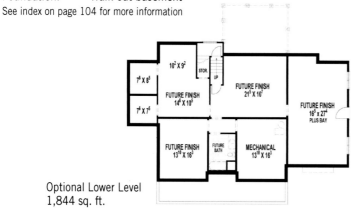

© Copyright by
designer/architect

Optional Lower Level
1,844 sq. ft.

First Floor
2,027 sq. ft.

Images provided by designer/architect

PLAN #904-101D-0056

Dimensions:	72' W x 77' D
Heated Sq. Ft.:	2,593
Bonus Sq. Ft.:	1,892
Bedrooms: 2	Bathrooms: 2½
Exterior Walls:	2" x 6"
Foundation:	Walk-out basement

See index on page 104 for more information

© Copyright by
designer/architect

Optional
Lower Level
1,892 sq. ft.

First Floor
2,593 sq. ft.

CALL 1-800-373-2646   **ONLINE** houseplansandmore.com

First Floor
2,510 sq. ft.

PLAN #904-056D-0096

Dimensions:	91'6" W x 70' D
Heated Sq. Ft.:	2,510
Bonus Sq. Ft.:	2,510
Bedrooms: 3	Bathrooms: 2½

Foundation: Walk-out basement standard; crawl space or slab for an additional fee

See index on page 104 for more information

Images provided by designer/architect

Optional
Lower Level
2,510 sq. ft.

Images provided by designer/architect

PLAN #904-032D-1124

Dimensions:	66' W x 50' D
Heated Sq. Ft.:	2,117
Bonus Sq. Ft.:	360
Bedrooms: 3	Bathrooms: 2
Exterior Walls:	2" x 6"

Foundation: Crawl space standard; basement, monolithic slab or floating slab for an additional fee

See index on page 104 for more information

BONUS ROOM
12-4 X 15-6

Optional
Second Floor
360 sq. ft.

First Floor
2,117 sq. ft.

PLAN #904-011D-0579

Dimensions: 60' W x 64' D
Heated Sq. Ft.: 2,292
Bedrooms: 3   Bathrooms: 2½
Exterior Walls: 2" x 6"
Foundation: Joisted crawl space or post & beam standard; slab or basement for an additional fee
See index on page 104 for more information

FEATURES

- Undeniable charm commands full attention with this modern farmhouse
- Once inside, the vaulted living area and dining area join forces and surround the kitchen with plenty of gathering space
- Charming extras can be found throughout this design including a built-in window seat in the dining area, and a bench and locker style storage in the mud room
- The vaulted master bedroom enjoys a first floor location and includes a large walk-in closet and a spacious bath with a walk-in shower and a spa style tub
- 2-car front entry garage

Images provided by designer/architect

Second Floor
544 sq. ft.

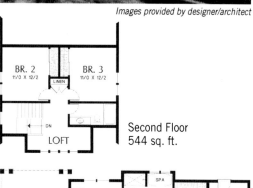

First Floor
1,748 sq. ft.

© Copyright by designer/architect

PLAN #904-024S-0024

Dimensions: 52' W x 62' D
Heated Sq. Ft.: 3,610
Bedrooms: 5   Bathrooms: 4
Foundation: Slab

See index on page 104 for more information

FEATURES

- This home is built with energy efficient windows and doors helping to keep it cooler in the summer and warmer in the winter
- The oversized porch enjoys a built-in sink and grill space for cooking outdoors
- The second floor sitting room makes a great spot for a computer area
- Two sets of double doors lead from the dining area to the covered porch creating a great set-up when entertaining
- The first floor master bedroom enjoys a spacious walk-in closet and private bath featuring a walk-in shower and a separate spa tub

Images provided by designer/architect

Second Floor
1,286 sq. ft.

First Floor
2,324 sq. ft.

© Copyright by designer/architect

PLAN #904-026D-1942

Dimensions: 40' W x 59' D
Heated Sq. Ft.: 2,509
Bedrooms: 4   Bathrooms: 3
Foundation: Basement standard;
crawl space, slab or walk-out
basement for an additional fee
See index on page 104 for more information

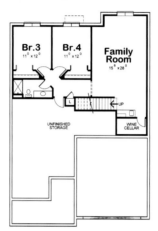

Lower Level
913 sq. ft.

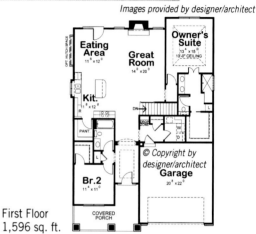

First Floor
1,596 sq. ft.

Second Floor
1,450 sq. ft.

First Floor
2,370 sq. ft.

PLAN #904-157D-0022

Dimensions: 62'6" W x 84'2" D
Heated Sq. Ft.: 3,820
Bonus Sq. Ft.: 359
Bedrooms: 5   Bathrooms: 4
Foundation: Crawl space standard;
slab for an additional fee
See index on page 104 for more information

CALL 1-800-373-2646   **ONLINE** houseplansandmore.com

Images provided by designer/architect

PLAN #904-020D-0386

Dimensions:	58' W x 50' D
Heated Sq. Ft.:	2,754
Bedrooms: 4	Bathrooms: 3
Exterior Walls:	2" x 6"
Foundation:	Walk-out basement

See index on page 104 for more information

© Copyright by designer/architect

Lower Level
1,134 sq. ft.

First Floor
1,620 sq. ft.

Images provided by designer/architect

PLAN #904-011D-0652

Dimensions:	40' W x 60' D
Heated Sq. Ft.:	2,448
Bedrooms: 3	Bathrooms: 2½
Exterior Walls:	2" x 6"

Foundation: Joisted continuous footings standard; basement for an additional fee

See index on page 104 for more information

© Copyright by designer/architect

Second Floor
1,092 sq. ft.

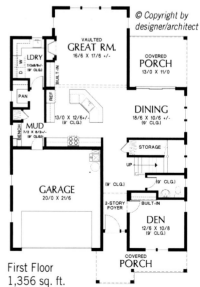

First Floor
1,356 sq. ft.

PLAN #904-028D-0097

Dimensions:	60' W x 53' D
Heated Sq. Ft.:	1,908
Bedrooms: 3	Bathrooms: 2
Exterior Walls:	2" x 6"
Foundation:	Slab

See index on page 104 for more information

FEATURES

- Small, yet incredibly stylish, this modern farmhouse is the perfect floor plan if you're looking for a split bedroom floor plan
- Step into a great room with double doors leading to the backyard
- The kitchen enjoys a corner walk-in pantry for keeping things tidy, an oversized farmhouse sink and a nearby dining area
- Two bedrooms share the full bath between them
- The laundry room is conveniently located off the kitchen
- 2-car front entry garage

Images provided by designer/architect

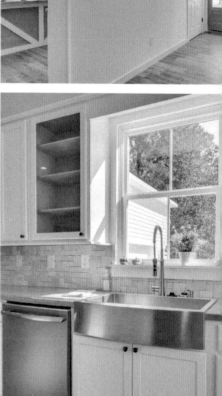

MASTER BEDROOM 18'-0" X 14'-0"

GREAT ROOM 18'-0"X18'-4"

MASTER BATH 13'-5" X 9'-6"

WIC

DINING AREA 14'-0" X 12'-0"

DOUBLE GARAGE 24'X20'

BEDROOM 2 12'-6" X 12'-0"

BATH 2

FOYER

KITCHEN 16'-0" X 16'-6"

© Copyright by designer/architect

BEDROOM 3 12'-6"X 12'-0"

PANTRY

6 FT. DEEP COVERED PORCH

Images provided by designer/architect

PLAN #904-055S-0115

Dimensions: 126'2" W x 110'11" D
Heated Sq. Ft.:   4,501
Bonus Sq. Ft.:   501
Bedrooms: 5   Bathrooms: 5½
Foundation: Crawl space or slab
standard; basement or daylight
basement for an additional fee
See index on page 104 for more information

FEATURES

- The two-story great room boasts
  double-doors that open to the
  rear covered porch, a fireplace,
  and built-in flanking shelves

- A walk-in pantry and a breakfast
  bar with seating for seven are
  some awesome features of the
  well-equipped kitchen

- The bonus room on the second
  floor has an additional 501 square
  feet of living area and is perfect
  for a home theater or game
  room

- 3-car front entry garage

Second Floor
1,103 sq. ft.

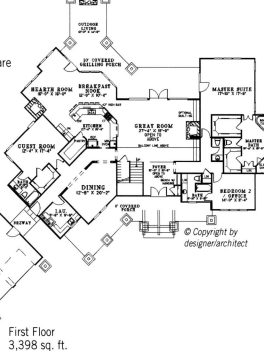
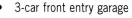

© Copyright by
designer/architect

First Floor
3,398 sq. ft.

PLAN #904-167D-0003

Dimensions:	50'6" W x 50'5" D
Heated Sq. Ft.:	2,569
Bedrooms:	4
Bathrooms:	3 full, 2 half
Exterior Walls:	2" x 6"

Foundation: Crawl space standard; basement or slab for additional fee

See index on page 104 for more information

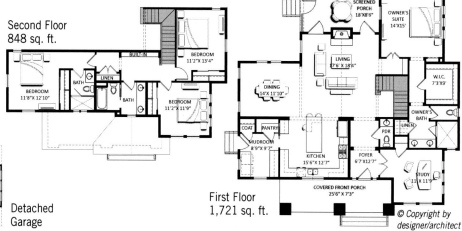

Second Floor
848 sq. ft.

First Floor
1,721 sq. ft.

© Copyright by designer/architect

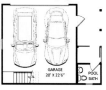

Detached Garage

PLAN #904-111D-0042

Dimensions:	29' W x 30' D
Heated Sq. Ft.:	1,074
Bedrooms: 3	Bathrooms: 2½
Exterior Walls:	2" x 6"

Foundation: Slab standard; crawl space for an additional fee

See index on page 104 for more information

First Floor
469 sq. ft.

© Copyright by designer/architect

Second Floor
605 sq. ft.

CALL 1-800-373-2646   ONLINE houseplansandmore.com

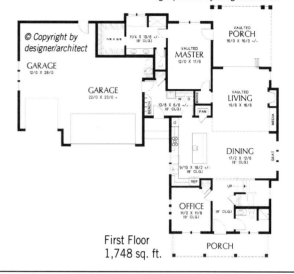

PLAN #904-011D-0646

Dimensions: 72' W x 66'4" D
Heated Sq. Ft.: 2,292
Bedrooms: 4   Bathrooms: 3
Exterior Walls: 2" x 6"
Foundation: Joisted crawl space
standard; slab or basement for an
additional fee

See index on page 104 for more information

Second Floor
544 sq. ft.

First Floor
1,748 sq. ft.

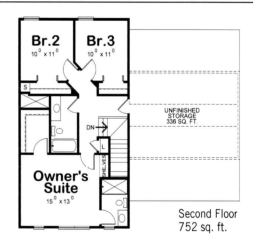

PLAN #904-026D-2079

Dimensions: 42' W x 42' D
Heated Sq. Ft.: 1,600
Bonus Sq. Ft.: 336
Bedrooms: 3   Bathrooms: 2½
Foundation: Basement standard;
crawl space, slab or walk-out
basement for an additional fee

See index on page 104 for more information

Second Floor
752 sq. ft.

First Floor
848 sq. ft.

PLAN #904-091D-0524

Dimensions: 69' W x 59' 6"D
Heated Sq. Ft.: 2,480
Bonus Sq. Ft.: 361
Bedrooms: 4   Bathrooms: 3½
Exterior Walls: 2" x 6"
Foundation: Basement standard;
crawl space or slab for an additional
fee

See index on page 104 for more information

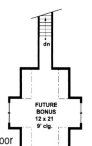

Optional
Second Floor
361 sq. ft.

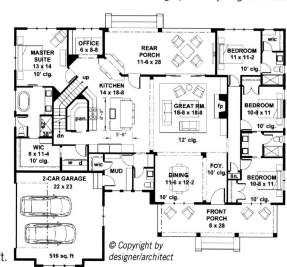

First Floor
2,480 sq. ft.

© Copyright by
designer/architect

© Copyright by designer/architect

PLAN #904-144D-0024

Dimensions: 32' W x 32' D
Heated Sq. Ft.: 1,024
Bedrooms: 1   Bathrooms: 1½
Exterior Walls: 2" x 6"
Foundation: Basement or daylight
basement standard; crawl space, slab
or walk-out basement for an
additional fee

See index on page 104 for more information

CALL 1-800-373-2646   **ONLINE** houseplansandmore.com

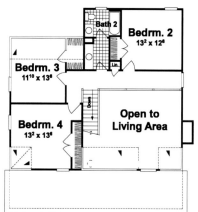

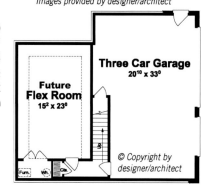

Second Floor
860 sq. ft.

PLAN #904-052D-0157

Images provided by designer/architect

Dimensions: 40'4" W x 42' D
Heated Sq. Ft.: 2,067
Bonus Sq. Ft.: 356
Bedrooms: 4   Bathrooms: 2½
Foundation: Walk-out basement
See index on page 104 for more information

Lower Level
88 sq. ft.

First Floor
1,119 sq. ft.

© Copyright by designer/architect

Second Floor
1,852 sq. ft.

PLAN #904-032D-1067

Images provided by designer/architect

Dimensions: 66' W x 50' D
Heated Sq. Ft.: 3,599
Bedrooms: 3   Bathrooms: 3
Exterior Walls: 2" x 6"
Foundation: Basement or crawl space
standard; floating slab or monolithic
slab for an additional fee
See index on page 104 for more information

© Copyright by designer/architect

First Floor
1,747 sq. ft.

designing & decorating a
MODERN FARMHOUSE
inside & out

Say goodbye to the days of the cookie-cutter style ranch homes when all subdivisions looked the same, today's homeowners are looking for a unique, simple and an uncluttered approach to residential design that uses an open-concept floor plan, and includes only the bare necessities, while relying on texture rather than color to create its iconic look. These design concepts are the heart and soul of the Modern Farmhouse.

Many architects and residential designers blame home and garden television channels, and fixer upper and do-it-yourself type shows for the advent of this unique residential style, but no matter who you credit for its creation, the Modern Farmhouse is a sensation sweeping the nation, and everyone looking to build a new home is falling in love with its undeniable personality. But, before you just select a Modern Farmhouse plan, do you know what makes a Modern Farmhouse truly what it is? There are several key design and decorating characteristics that make a Modern Farmhouse all its own.

on the outside

HIGH PITCHED Modern Farmhouse style uses a gable roof in a steeper pitch than a typical home built in the last two or three decades. This is a popular feature because it allows for higher, more dramatic vaulted ceilings in the interior, while in turn, opening up spaces and making them feel larger. When steep gables aren't being used, then a flat roof is often added to the mix.

ALL ABOUT TEXTURE Although simple in overall design, subtle texture really takes a prominent role in the look and feel of a modern farmhouse. Board and batten (also called clapboard siding), vertical and horizontal siding, a steel roof, and even a small amount of brick or stone all combine to create a modern farmhouse that feels fresh and new, while still feeling a bit nostalgic to the traditional and timeless farmhouse style.

COLOR, WHAT COLOR? Most often white is the color of choice for the exterior, but gray and other neutral colors are also popular for both the interior and the exterior. Black and natural wood tones also have a role in the finished look. Color takes a supporting role to all of the texture provided by the various siding styles being used.

ONE-OF-A-KIND DESIGN Farmhouses of the past were utilitarian and usually rectangular in shape. These homes were built simply in order to allow for quick construction and so a dwelling could be created for a family ready to work their land. Construction had to be done around the growing cycles, so the designs were modest and straightforward. Today's Modern Farmhouses still have a common simplicity similar to their previous counterparts, yet many have varied roof lines, an L-shape, or the look of multiple buildings, which promotes additional natural light in the interior because there are more exterior walls for extra windows and doors.

LOVE THE OUTDOORS Often referred to as "outdoor living spaces," large front and back covered porches are common and an important feature because they offer additional living space for dining, entertaining, or relaxing. Add a porch swing, or an updated rocking chair in black or a vibrant color, and these porches are less "Grandma's house," and more today's modern family.

STAY TRANSPARENT As discussed, windows are an important design element that allow for the interior to feel light and airy. Typically, double-hung and seen with black framing that stands out against the stark white exterior and interior finishes, windows play an important role in keeping the home bright, friendly and open. Traditional double-hung style keep the design grounded to its original farmhouse roots.

on the inside

LESS IS MORE The modern farmhouse has a laid-back personality that's friendly, inviting, and promotes a simple lifestyle. Homeowners now more than ever want their homes to be a refuge from the stress in their daily lives. Traffic, email, social media, and other constant distractions create chaos homeowners are looking to escape from. A Modern Farmhouse is meant to be a peaceful, inviting retreat, somewhat like a sanctuary that shelters from the outside noise. Even the floor plans are designed to maintain a sense of openness with very few walls. Large windows throughout add natural light, and larger spaces for effortless daily living like spacious mud and laundry rooms are quite popular. Think clean and functional.

NEUTRAL BY NATURE The interior of the modern farmhouse mimics the exterior and sticks with a neutral color palette that's airy and bright. In addition to the most popular color, which is white; soft gray, beige and blue are used promoting a sense of tranquility.

RECLAIMING DESIGN INTEGRITY

With the popularity of using reclaimed wood and other architectural design elements from buildings of the past, it makes perfect sense that Modern Farmhouse style incorporates these unique features. From rustic timber beams and rafters, to the current favorite wall paneling affectionately called "Ship Lap," although the overall color palette may be white or neutral, rustic elements are often used for architectural interest. Even steel and polished concrete have a place in these homes because of their industrial look and durability.

KITCHEN DESIGN

A modern farmhouse kitchen is the heart of the home. It is a special place where a family will eat, socialize and relax together. These kitchens are open to the surrounding spaces, have a neutral color palette, which is usually white. They include several windows, Shaker-style cabinets, white marble or quartz countertops, subway tile, Industrial-style or Edison light fixtures, a large island for cooking and casual dining, and open shelving. Think uncomplicated and less cluttered.

HOME DECOR

The accessories in a Modern Farmhouse are not matching, but are more complementary with character. Modern Farmhouse décor uses carefully placed, thoughtful elements that add personality to a space. The decor mixes sleek, modern accessories with timeless ones. Artwork may be the one thing that adds a pop of color. The majority of the texture comes from throw rugs, and the fabric used on the sofas and chairs. Bold light fixtures, and natural wood floors are a must, and if you're looking for a sleeker vibe, then add some steel, wrought iron, and other metals to create an Industrial feel.

BARN DOORS GALORE

Besides being a stylish space-saving option, barn-style doors can be a rustic addition when using natural wood, or paint it white or a color and add black hardware for a more sleek look. Either way, "barn doors" are a staple in Modern Farmhouses and offer plenty of character while taking up less space.

If you're enthralled with Modern Farmhouse style, you are not alone. This style is the darling of residential architecture today and it's easy to see why. It combines so many wonderful features to create something so utterly simple and effortless. Thoughtful, subdued, smart, and functional all met their match with the invention of the Modern Farmhouse, and we think it was about time.

Images provided by designer/architect

PLAN #904-051D-0962

Dimensions: 82'4" W x 70' D
Heated Sq. Ft.: 3,205
Bedrooms: 4   Bathrooms: 4
Exterior Walls: 2" x 6"
Foundation: Basement standard;
crawl space or slab for an additional
fee

See index on page 104 for more information

© Copyright by designer/architect

First Floor
2,265 sq. ft.

Second Floor
940 sq. ft.

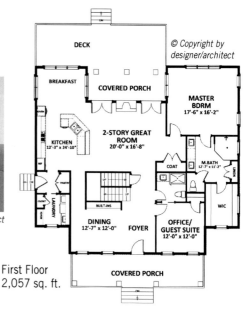

Second Floor
1,153 sq. ft.

First Floor
2,057 sq. ft.

PLAN #904-139D-0061

Dimensions: 51' W x 63'8" D
Heated Sq. Ft.: 3,210
Bedrooms: 4   Bathrooms: 4
Exterior Walls: 2" x 6"
Foundation: Crawl space standard;
slab, basement, daylight basement or
walk-out basement for an additional
fee

See index on page 104 for more information

Images provided by designer/architect

CALL 1-800-373-2646   ONLINE houseplansandmore.com

PLAN #904-155D-0147

Dimensions: 70'6" W x 58'2" D
Heated Sq. Ft.: 2,073
Bonus Sq. Ft.: 316
Bedrooms: 3   Bathrooms: 2½
Foundation: Crawl space or slab
standard; basement or daylight
basement for an additional fee

See index on page 104 for more information

Optional
Second Floor
316 sq. ft.

First Floor
2,073 sq. ft.

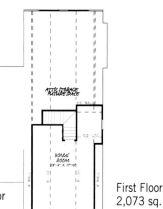

PLAN #904-091D-0509

Dimensions: 72' W x 69'2" D
Heated Sq. Ft.: 2,886
Bonus Sq. Ft.: 270
Bedrooms: 4   Bathrooms: 3½
Exterior Walls: 2" x 6"
Foundation: Basement or crawl space
standard; slab or walk-out basement
for an additional fee

See index on page 104 for more information

Second Floor
1,086 sq. ft.

First Floor
1,800 sq. ft.

Second Floor
1,144 sq. ft.

PLAN #904-139D-0088

Dimensions: 63'7" W x 61'6" D
Heated Sq. Ft.: 3,121
Bonus Sq. Ft.: 461
Bedrooms: 3   Bathrooms: 2½
Exterior Walls: 2" x 6"
Foundation: Crawl space standard; slab, basement, daylight basement or walk-out basement for an additional fee

See index on page 104 for more information

Images provided by designer/architect

First Floor
1,977 sq. ft.

© Copyright by designer/architect

Images provided by designer/architect

PLAN #904-155D-0129

Dimensions: 70'4" W x 56'2" D
Heated Sq. Ft.: 2,220
Bonus Sq. Ft.: 432
Bedrooms: 4   Bathrooms: 3
Foundation: Crawl space or slab standard; basement or daylight basement for an additional fee

See index on page 104 for more information

© Copyright by designer/architect

Optional
Second Floor
432 sq. ft.

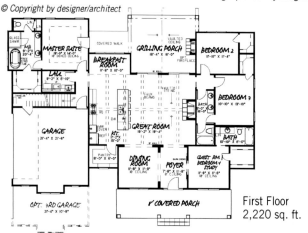

First Floor
2,220 sq. ft.

CALL 1-800-373-2646   ONLINE houseplansandmore.com

PLAN #904-091D-0508

Dimensions:	72' W x 65'2" D
Heated Sq. Ft.:	2,528
Bonus Sq. Ft.:	430
Bedrooms: 4	Bathrooms: 3½
Exterior Walls:	2" x 6"

Foundation: Basement or crawl space standard; daylight basement for an additional fee

See index on page 104 for more information

First Floor
1,732 sq. ft.

Second Floor
796 sq. ft.

Second Floor
1,516 sq. ft.

PLAN #904-032D-1069

Dimensions:	84' W x 49'6" D
Heated Sq. Ft.:	3,532
Bonus Sq. Ft.:	598
Bedrooms: 4	Bathrooms: 3½
Exterior Walls:	2" x 6"

Foundation: Crawl space, basement or walk-out basement standard; monolithic slab or floating slab for an additional fee

See index on page 104 for more information

First Floor
2,016 sq. ft.

PLAN #904-011D-0630

Dimensions:	90' W x 75' D
Heated Sq. Ft.:	2,495
Bedrooms: 3	Bathrooms: 2½
Exterior Walls:	2" x 6"

Foundation: Post & beam or joisted
continuous footings standard; slab or
basement for an additional fee
See index on page 104 for more information

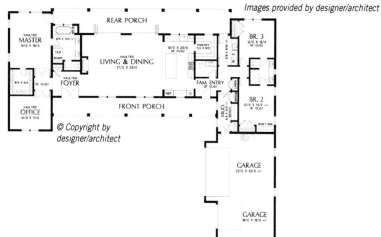

© Copyright by
designer/architect

PLAN #904-051D-0979

Dimensions:	81' W x 59' D
Heated Sq. Ft.:	1,921
Bedrooms: 3	Bathrooms: 2
Exterior Walls:	2" x 6"

Foundation: Basement standard;
crawl space or slab for an additional
fee
See index on page 104 for more information

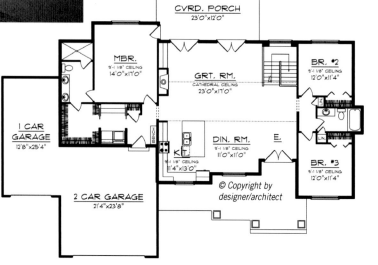

© Copyright by
designer/architect

CALL 1-800-373-2646   **ONLINE** houseplansandmore.com

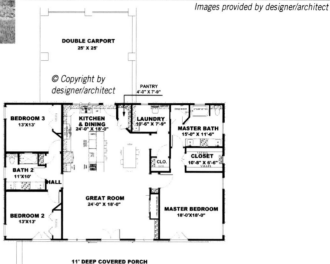

Images provided by designer/architect

PLAN #904-028D-0104

Dimensions:	60' W x 72' D
Heated Sq. Ft.:	2,160
Bedrooms: 3	Bathrooms: 2
Exterior Walls:	2" x 6"

Foundation: Slab or basement, please specify when ordering

See index on page 104 for more information

DOUBLE CARPORT
25' X 25'

© Copyright by designer/architect

PANTRY
4'-0" X 7'-9"

BEDROOM 3
13'X13'

KITCHEN & DINING
24'-0" X 18'-0"

LAUNDRY
10'-6" X 7'-9"

MASTER BATH
15'-0" X 11'-6"

CLO.

CLOSET
10'-8" X 6'-6"

BATH 2
11'X10'

HALL

GREAT ROOM
24'-0" X 18'-0"

MASTER BEDROOM
18'-0"X18'-0"

BEDROOM 2
13'X13'

11' DEEP COVERED PORCH

Images provided by designer/architect

PLAN #904-011D-0661

Dimensions:	76' W x 62' D
Heated Sq. Ft.:	2,508
Bedrooms: 3	Bathrooms: 2½
Exterior Walls:	2" x 6"

Foundation: Joisted continuous footings standard; basement for an additional fee

See index on page 104 for more information

© Copyright by designer/architect

PATIO

VAULTED OUTDOOR LIVING
18/0 X 18/0 +/-

OUTDOOR KITCHEN

BR. 2
11/0 X 13/8
(9' CLG.)

NOOK
11/0 X 11/0 +/-
(10' CLG.)

VAULTED MASTER
13/8 X 17/0

VAULTED GREAT RM.
17/0 X 23/0

BR. 3
11/8 X 14/8
(9' CLG.)

STORAGE
6/0 X 3/6

PANTRY
9/2 X 5/10

GARAGE
23/0 X 28/0 +/-

DRESSING
11/2 X 11/8+/-
(10' CLG.)

TILE SHWR

FOYER
7/0 X 11/0
(10' CLG.)

DINING
14/8 X 11/6
(10' CLG.)

PORCH

PLAN #904-028D-0113

Dimensions:	68' W x 84' D
Heated Sq. Ft.:	2,582
Bedrooms: 3	Bathrooms: 2½
Exterior Walls:	2" x 6"
Foundation:	Basement

See index on page 104 for more information

FEATURES

- This stylish Modern Farmhouse has terrific symmetry and curb appeal
- There are two covered porches; one in the front and one in the back and both are 8' deep
- The vaulted great room has a cathedral ceiling and a centered fireplace as a focal point
- The kitchen has an eating bar and nearby dining space
- The private master bedroom has a walk-in closet and a private bath with walk-in shower as well as a oversized spa tub
- There are two additional bedrooms on the opposite side of the home that share a full bath and have their own walk-in closets
- A walk-in linen closet, a walk-in pantry and a laundry room help keep family life organized
- There's an additional room called, "owner's choice" that offers space for a multitude of needs including a home office, play room or hobby space
- 2-car side entry garage

Images provided by designer/architect

CALL 1-800-373-2646   **ONLINE** houseplansandmore.com

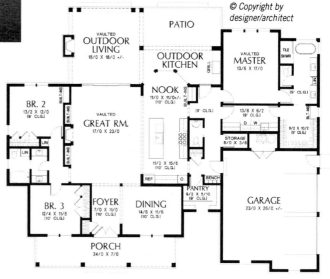

© Copyright by designer/architect

PLAN #904-011D-0662

Dimensions: 76' W x 62' D
Heated Sq. Ft.: 2,460
Bedrooms: 3   Bathrooms: 2½
Exterior Walls: 2" x 6"
Foundation: Joisted continuous footings

See index on page 104 for more information

PLAN #904-077D-0288

Dimensions: 57' W x 74' D
Heated Sq. Ft.: 2,107
Bonus Sq. Ft.: 461
Bedrooms: 3   Bathrooms: 2½
Foundation: Crawl space or slab, please specify when ordering

See index on page 104 for more information

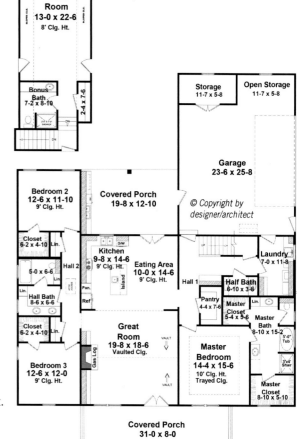

Optional Second Floor 461 sq. ft.

© Copyright by designer/architect

First Floor 2,107 sq. ft.

CALL 1-800-373-2646   ONLINE houseplansandmore.com

PLAN #904-144D-0023

Dimensions: 58' W x 32'" D
Heated Sq. Ft.: 928
Bedrooms: 2   Bathrooms: 2
Foundation: Crawl space or slab
standard; basement or daylight
basement for an additional fee
See index on page 104 for more information

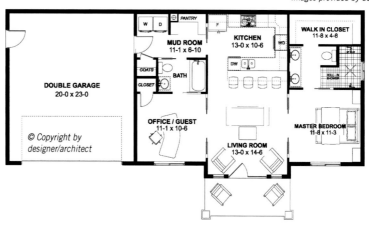

DOUBLE GARAGE
20-0 x 23-0

PANTRY
MUD ROOM
11-1 x 6-10
KITCHEN
13-0 x 10-6
WALK IN CLOSET
11-8 x 4-8
COATS
BATH
CLOSET
OFFICE / GUEST
11-1 x 10-6
MASTER BEDROOM
11-8 x 11-3
LIVING ROOM
13-0 x 14-6

© Copyright by
designer/architect

PLAN #904-032D-0887

Dimensions: 42' W x 40' D
Heated Sq. Ft.: 1,212
Bonus Sq. Ft.: 1,212
Bedrooms: 2   Bathrooms: 1
Exterior Walls: 2" x 6"
Foundation: Basement standard;
crawl space, monolithic slab or
floating slab for an additional fee
See index on page 104 for more information

Optional Lower Level
1,212 sq. ft.

© Copyright by
designer/architect

First Floor
1,212 sq. ft.

26'-0" x 10'-0"

14'-9" x 15'-0"

25'-8" x 20'-9"

8'-8" x 10'-8"

PLAN #904-101D-0080

Dimensions: 79' W x 97'9" D
Heated Sq. Ft.: 2,682
Bonus Sq. Ft.: 1,940
Bedrooms: 2   Bathrooms: 2½
Exterior Walls: 2" x 6"
Foundation: Basement, daylight basement or walk-out basement, please specify when ordering
See index on page 104 for more information

Images provided by designer/architect

FEATURES

- This rambling ranch home typifies the best in today's design with unique architectural features
- Family gatherings can enjoy the outdoors thanks to expansive rear decks, one complete with a fireplace
- A private den with deck access is a secluded retreat when working from home
- The optional lower level has an additional 1,940 square feet of living area including three bedrooms, two baths, a laundry room, and a rec room
- 3-car side entry garage

© Copyright by designer/architect

First Floor
2,682 sq. ft.

Optional
Lower Level
1,940 sq. ft.

PLAN #904-155D-0070

Images provided by designer/architect

Dimensions: 60' W x 80'8" D
Heated Sq. Ft.: 2,464
Bonus Sq. Ft.: 758
Bedrooms: 4 Bathrooms: 3½
Foundation: Crawl space or slab standard; basement or daylight basement for an additional fee
See index on page 104 for more information

FEATURES

- The best in Farmhouse living, this home has a welcoming covered front porch and a rear grilling porch
- Decorative columns accent the private dining room, perfect for special events
- The combining of the great room, kitchen and breakfast room create a space that no doubt will be the central hub of this home
- The master suite offers all the amenities a homeowner needs
- The private bedroom 4 has its own bath and built-in desk
- The bonus area on the second floor has an additional 758 square feet of living area
- 2-car side entry garage

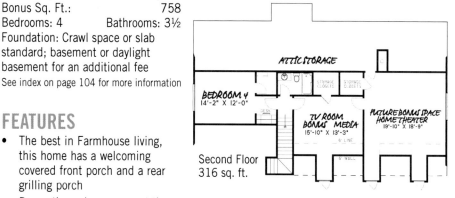

Second Floor
316 sq. ft.

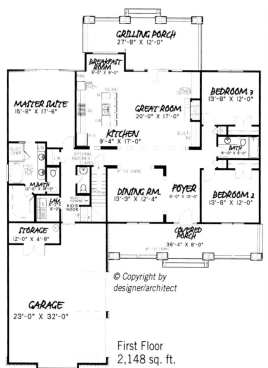

© Copyright by designer/architect

First Floor
2,148 sq. ft.

PLAN #904-032D-1078

Dimensions:	48' W x 50' D
Heated Sq. Ft.:	3,497
Bedrooms: 5	Bathrooms: 3½
Exterior Walls:	2" x 6"

Foundation: Basement or crawl space standard; floating slab or monolithic slab for an additional fee

See index on page 104 for more information

© Copyright by designer/architect

First Floor
1,517 sq. ft.

Second Floor
1,980 sq. ft.

PLAN #904-139D-0089

Dimensions:	94'5" W x 94'8" D
Heated Sq. Ft.:	3,734
Bonus Sq. Ft.:	679
Bedrooms:	4
Bathrooms:	3 full, 3 half
Exterior Walls:	2" x 6"

Foundation: Crawl space standard; slab, basement, daylight basement or walk-out basement for an additional fee

See index on page 104 for more information

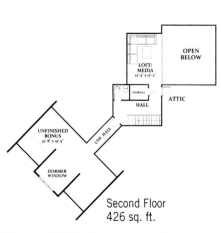

© Copyright by designer/architect

First Floor
3,308 sq. ft.

Second Floor
426 sq. ft.

CALL 1-800-373-2646   **ONLINE** houseplansandmore.com

PLAN #904-155D-0118

Dimensions: 121'6" W x 65'7" D
Heated Sq. Ft.: 3,310
Bedrooms: 4 Bathrooms: 3½
Foundation: Crawl space or slab
standard; daylight basement or
basement for an additional fee

See index on page 104 for more information

© Copyright by
designer/architect

First Floor
2,301 sq. ft.

Second Floor
1,009 sq. ft.

PLAN #904-011D-0650

Dimensions: 60' W x 53' D
Heated Sq. Ft.: 2,213
Bonus Sq. Ft.: 442
Bedrooms: 3 Bathrooms: 2
Exterior Walls: 2" x 6"
Foundation: Joisted crawl space
standard; basement for an additional
fee

See index on page 104 for more information

First Floor
2,213 sq. ft.

© Copyright by
designer/architect

Optional
Second Floor
442 sq. ft.

PLAN #904-051D-0960

Dimensions: 117' W x 50'8" D
Heated Sq. Ft.:   2,784
Bedrooms: 3   Bathrooms: 2
Exterior Walls: 2" x 6"
Foundation: Basement standard; crawl space or slab for an additional fee
See index on page 104 for more information

FEATURES

- This ranch home design is sure to win you over with its very classy exterior
- You are welcomed into the home with eleven-foot ceilings that top the great room and kitchen
- All three bedrooms, including the master bedroom, are located on the right side of the home
- The master bedroom includes a bath with a spa style tub, and dual sinks, as well as a spacious walk-in closet
- The secondary bedrooms share a full bath nearby
- The three-stall garage is located on the left side of the house with a large screened-in porch behind it
- 3-car front entry garage

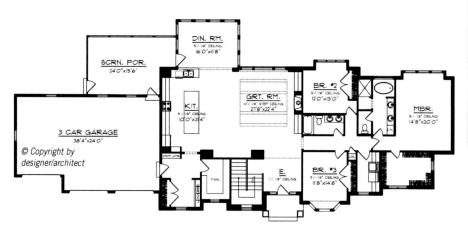

Images provided by designer/architect

CALL 1-800-373-2646   **ONLINE** houseplansandmore.com

PLAN #904-055D-0990

Dimensions: 113' W x 95'8" D
Heated Sq. Ft.: 2,555
Bonus Sq. Ft.: 509
Bedrooms: 4   Bathrooms: 3
Foundation: Crawl space or slab standard; basement or daylight basement for an additional fee

See index on page 104 for more information

Images provided by designer/architect

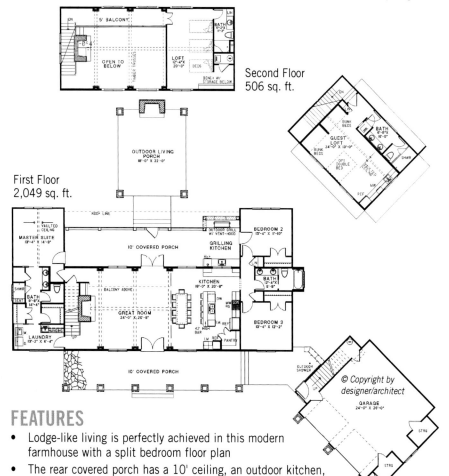

Second Floor
506 sq. ft.

First Floor
2,049 sq. ft.

© Copyright by designer/architect

FEATURES

- Lodge-like living is perfectly achieved in this modern farmhouse with a split bedroom floor plan
- The rear covered porch has a 10' ceiling, an outdoor kitchen, and leads to a remote outdoor living porch with a fireplace
- The master suite has direct access to the laundry room making this chore a lot easier to tackle
- Above the garage is a guest suite with an additional 509 square feet of living area featuring a bath and privacy that will be appreciated when people visit
- 2-car front entry garage

PLAN #904-028D-0108

Dimensions: 33' W x 40' D
Heated Sq. Ft.:   890
Bedrooms: 2   Bathrooms: 1
Exterior Walls: 2" x 6"
Foundation: Crawl space or slab,
please specify when ordering
See index on page 104 for more information

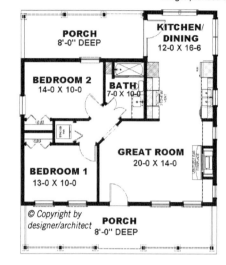

PORCH
8'-0" DEEP

KITCHEN/
DINING
12-0 X 16-6

BEDROOM 2
14-0 X 10-0

BATH
7-0 X 10-0

GREAT ROOM
20-0 X 14-0

BEDROOM 1
13-0 X 10-0

© Copyright by
designer/architect

PORCH
8'-0" DEEP

PLAN #904-032D-0935

Dimensions: 24' W x 24' D
Heated Sq. Ft.:   1,050
Bedrooms: 2   Bathrooms: 1½
Exterior Walls: 2" x 6"
Foundation: Basement standard;
floating slab, crawl space or
monolithic slab for an additional fee
See index on page 104 for more information

Second Floor
474 sq. ft.

10'-2" X 9'-0"
3,05 X 2,70

12'-0" X 11'-0"
3,60 X 3,30

11'-8" X 10'-4"
3,50 X 3,10

22'-8" X 12'-4"
6,80 X 3,70

© Copyright by
designer/architect

First Floor
576 sq. ft.

CALL 1-800-373-2646   **ONLINE** houseplansandmore.com

PLAN #904-011D-0657

Dimensions: 26' W x 34' D
Heated Sq. Ft.: 1,394
Bedrooms: 3   Bathrooms: 2½
Exterior Walls: 2" x 6"
Foundation: Joisted crawl space standard; basement for an additional fee

See index on page 104 for more information

PATIO

DINING
9/6 X 10/6 +/-
(9' CLG.)

12/8 X 12/8 +/-
(9' CLG.)

LIN

REF

STOR

D · W

PAN

LIVING
15/0 X 14/6 +/-
(9' CLG.)

UP

COVERED
PORCH
22/0 X 6/0

First Floor
714 sq. ft.

MASTER
13/0 X 12/8

LIN

DN

BR. 2
12/0 X 10/6 +/-

BR. 3
10/4 X 10/6

Second Floor
680 sq. ft.

© Copyright by designer/architect

PLAN #904-121D-0011

Dimensions: 68'4" W x 56' D
Heated Sq. Ft.: 2,241
Bedrooms: 4   Bathrooms: 2½
Foundation: Basement standard; crawl space or slab for an additional fee

See index on page 104 for more information

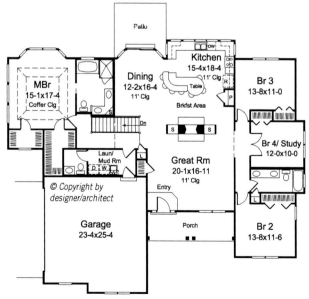

Patio

Kitchen
15-4x18-4
11' Clg

Dining
12-2x16-4
11' Clg

Brkfst Area

R

P

MBr
15-1x17-4
Coffer Clg

Laun/
Mud Rm

Br 3
13-8x11-0

Br 4/ Study
12-0x10-0

Great Rm
20-1x16-11
11' Clg

Entry

Dn

S

S

Br 2
13-8x11-6

Garage
23-4x25-4

Porch

© Copyright by designer/architect

PLAN #904-032D-0963

Dimensions:	34' W x 38' D
Heated Sq. Ft.:	1,178
Bonus Sq. Ft.:	1,178
Bedrooms: 1	Bathrooms: 1
Exterior Walls:	2" x 6"

Foundation: Basement standard; crawl space, floating slab or monolithic slab for an additional fee
See index on page 104 for more information

Images provided by designer/architect

FEATURES

- This stylish smaller modern farmhouse inspired home takes simplicity and style to a new level
- Step into an oversized entry hall from the charming covered porch and discover an oversized walk-in closet for keeping the entry clutter-free
- The open-concept floor plan allows the kitchen and dining space to blend perfectly with the main living area
- The kitchen features a large walk-in pantry with a barn style door for that rustic modern farmhouse feel
- The bedroom enjoys close proximity to the pampering bath that features a shower as well as a free-standing tub in one corner
- The optional lower level has an additional 1,178 square feet of living area

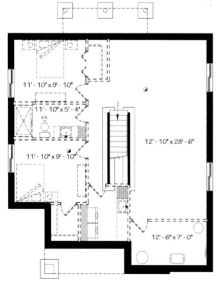

Optional Lower Level
1,178 sq. ft.

First Floor
1,178 sq. ft.

© Copyright by
designer/architect

PLAN #904-084D-0085

Dimensions: 85' W x 64' D
Heated Sq. Ft.:   2,252
Bonus Sq. Ft.:   1,341
Bedrooms: 3   Bathrooms: 2
Foundation: Slab standard; crawl
space for an additional fee
See index on page 104 for more information

Images provided by designer/architect

FEATURES

- Enter the great room from the covered front porch and discover an inviting space with a fireplace that is entirely open to a spacious beamed dining room and beyond to a large kitchen with an island

- A pleasing split bedroom floor plan offers privacy to everyone

- The master bedroom is spacious and has a large box-bay window with a window seat, a private bath with a free-standing tub as well as an oversized walk-in shower, and a sizable walk-in closet

- The rear covered porch has a vaulted ceiling and an outdoor kitchen, great for summertime get-togethers

- The optional second floor has an additional 1,341 square feet of living area ideal for a game room, home theater or guest space

- 2-car side entry garage

Optional
Second Floor
1,341 sq. ft.

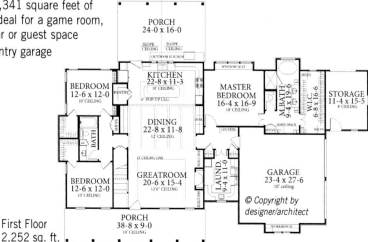

First Floor
2,252 sq. ft.

Images provided by designer/architect

PLAN #904-032D-0877

Dimensions: 38' W x 48' D
Heated Sq. Ft.: 1,283
Bedrooms: 2   Bathrooms: 1
Exterior Walls: 2" x 6"
Foundation: Basement standard;
crawl space, floating slab or
monolithic slab for an additional fee
See index on page 104 for more information

© Copyright by designer/architect

Images provided by designer/architect

PLAN #904-139D-0091

Dimensions: 64'5" W x 83'9" D
Heated Sq. Ft.: 3,163
Bonus Sq. Ft.: 447
Bedrooms: 4   Bathrooms: 3½
Exterior Walls: 2" x 6"
Foundation: Crawl space standard;
slab, basement, daylight basement or
walk-out basement for an additional
fee
See index on page 104 for more information

© Copyright by designer/architect

First Floor
2,362 sq. ft.

Second Floor
801 sq. ft.

CALL 1-800-373-2646   ONLINE houseplansandmore.com

Garage
23-4x23-4

© Copyright by designer/architect

Images provided by designer/architect

PLAN #904-121D-0025

Dimensions: 50' W x 34'6" D
Heated Sq. Ft.: 1,368
Bedrooms: 3   Bathrooms: 2
Foundation: Basement standard; crawl space or slab for an additional fee

See index on page 104 for more information

Patio

MBr
14-1x12-10
Coffer
Opt Vault

Kit
8-2x
12-6

Dining
11-9x12-6
Vaulted

Br 2
11-6x10-4

Br 3
10-2x10-4

Great Rm
20-3x15-0
Vaulted

Porch

Images provided by designer/architect

PLAN #904-084D-0082

Dimensions: 59'8" W x 54'3" D
Heated Sq. Ft.: 1,599
Bedrooms: 3   Bathrooms: 2
Foundation: Slab standard; crawl space for an additional fee

See index on page 104 for more information

PORCH
14-2 x 16-5
10' ceiling

GARAGE
24-4 x 23-3
10' ceiling

BEDROOM
11-3 x 11-3
10' ceiling

KITCHEN/DINING
21-8 x 11-4
10' ceiling

© Copyright by designer/architect

LAUN.
6-7 x 7-6

M.BATH
12-4 x 10-10
10' ceiling

BATH

LIVING
19-4 x 19-6
12' ceiling

MASTER BEDROOM
16-3 x 13-4
10' ceiling

M.Closet
6-8 x 10-0

BEDROOM
11-3 x 11-4
10' ceiling

PORCH
35-0 x 6-3

stylish & functional
LAUNDRY & MUD ROOMS

When it comes to starting the day right, most homeowners would agree that seeking lost keys and stumbling over wayward toys are not on the list of things to do.

Homeowners everywhere dream of a home where the day's necessary items are easily accessed without frustration or extreme exertion. Imagine the surprise when this dream becomes a reality – all it takes is some creative organization and attention to routine.

For many homeowners the front entryway is no longer the primary center of traffic for entering or exiting the home. Garage entries allow families to pile immediately into vehicles upon take-off and subsequently spill back into the house when landing back at home. Mud rooms and laundry areas have become the "catch alls," teaming with belongings that have no home or are forgotten upon drop-off. Day after day, this constantly growing clutter makes it more difficult to get in and out of the house efficiently. In order to combat the expanding mess (and increasing stress), it is time to take control of your mud room or laundry room space in just a few simple steps.

evaluate your needs

Before you even glance at the mud room, sit down and construct a list of every item that leaves your house daily. Break it down by person to evaluate each family member's individual needs. Then turn it around and create a second list with each item that regularly enters the house (again, by person). It may sound tedious, but this approach will help ensure that regularly needed belongings will have a place in your newly organized space.

With lists in hand, it is time to turn toward the space itself. What does the area need to make the lives of your family easier? Is there adequate floor space to install seating for removing muddy shoes? Is closet space accessible, or will you need to install a storage system? Keep in mind that each item needs a designated space to reside without stuffing or overflowing, so take your time researching what hardware can best serve your needs.

these storage solutions can include:

HOOKS are great for storing objects that require easy access on the move, such as keys, purses, umbrellas, or even dog leashes.

SHELVING UNITS such as cubbies and locker systems come in various sizes making them useful in virtually any rear foyer space. Whether supplementary storage for a closet, or the primary source of sorting and storing gear, these units can be customized to help maintain belongings for every member of your family.

BASKETS AND BINS come in numerous shapes, sizes, and materials, allowing your family to divide items efficiently. Clear, over-the-door hangers, are ideal for sorting small items like hats and mittens, making use of vertical space and keeping everything in sight.

cull the clutter

After you have devised what you need, it is time to remove what you do not. Begin cleaning out the current space, banishing those objects that do not belong in the entryway. Be careful to not let them pile up elsewhere! Make a rule that every item removed from the space is given a proper home; putting forth a small effort now will save time in the future.

Also use this time to categorize certain belongings and seek out a better storage spot. For example, if closet space is limited, is it really necessary to store infrequently used dress coats in the entryway? It makes much more sense to limit that closet to everyday wear while relocating the dress coats to another storage space.

move forward - slowly

Now that you know what storage is needed, "installation" can begin. Take your time and be deliberate with your placements. Slowly adjusting to your new space allows your family to form a routine, ensuring your rear foyer is used to its fullest capacity.

re-evaulate

While establishing a routine allows your family to get the most from a storage system, it is important to re-evaluate your organizational needs regularly. Upon examination, is each space still being utilized as intended? Have you noticed any frustrations with the system? For example, are there hooks for backpacks, but no place to store this season's sports bag? If one storage solution is not as convenient as before, this is your opportunity to try something else. As life changes so will your storage needs, so be on the look out for reoccurring issues and easy resolutions.

Unless noted, all images copyrighted by designer/architect. Page 48: top to bottom: Erin Crain Interiors, erincrain.com, Bernard Andre, photographer; Plan #101D-0088; Page 49, top, left: Plan #051D-0963; top, right: Better Homes & Gardens®; Plan #055D-1075; ClosetMaid® System, closetmaid.com; Plan #071S-0002; Page 50, top to bottom, left: ClosetMaid® Drop Zone Center, closetmaid. com; Electronic charging station, ikea.com; Plan #051D-0964; Plan #055D-0990; top to bottom, right: thehappyhousie.com; lookwhat-idid.blogspot.ca; Plan #101D-0061, Warren Diggles Photography; Page 51, top to bottom: washer and dryer, designamerica.com; ClosteMaid® Built-In Hamper, closetmaid.com; meritagehomes.com; Built-In Dog Food Bowls, Terracotta Design Build, terracottadesign-build.com; Built-In Cage and Dog Bed, maisonderevebuilders.com; All plans available for purchase at houseplansandmore.com.

just drop it

Beyond the need for organization of shoes, coats, bags, and other daily gear, some homeowners find themselves in need of a separate "drop zone," or a message center. Drop zones are typically a three to four foot wide surface where small items are kept organized. Valets keep charger cords under control and accessible, and small dishes or hooks organize different sets of keys. The drop zone is an excellent place to toss junk mail into a recycle bin while keeping important letters handy in a mail tray. If drawers are available, drop zones can also be used to store emergency items, spare keys, and extra office supplies.

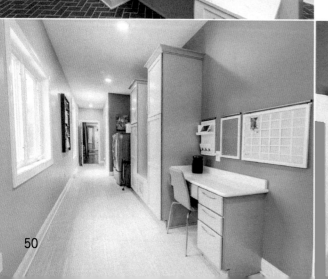

commanding performance

Message centers may or may not be a part of the drop zone depending on the space available. For some families, a simple white board is perfect for passing information and tracking one another's daily activities. Other families may expand the message center to utilize cork, magnet boards, or chalkboards while keeping track of schedules, notes, homework, grocery and chore lists. Whatever the use, the message center can play a vital role in keeping your home running smoothly.

Making the most of your mud room is not a difficult task, but it does require an initial time investment. Putting in time now will certainly save you future headaches and wasted efforts. Research the available storage options and seek suggestions from friends and even organizational professionals. As you begin this process, remember that there is not one "perfect" method for organizing your rear foyer. However, a little patience and flexibility will certainly help you find the best solution for your lifestyle.

the down & dirty on great
LAUNDRY ROOMS

Many homeowners recall when laundry rooms were located in unfinished basements, spare closets, or limited space found in the garage or kitchen. These laundry areas were often cramped, impractical, and continuously frustrating for families. Though it's often a task that is approached with little enthusiasm, today's home designs are embracing laundry and mud rooms and making them the most functional spaces under a home's roof. In order to arrange the most efficient laundry area in your home, below are a few aspects to keep in mind.

function

Heavy traffic areas can include the laundry facilities as long as there is adequate space. Even the most organized laundry room has a tendency to harbor piles of clothing, which are inconvenient with people moving through the space often. So, if you have a combined mud room/laundry room consider placing the laundry portion of the space as far from the entry as possible for better function and ease of movement. Install bins or hampers for dirty clothes and towels to avoid clothing piling up on the floor. Many homes have multiple hampers, with each family member being responsible for gathering their dirty items. If space allows, place a sorter in the laundry room with each slot dedicated to various laundry loads that family members can sort in an organized fashion.

Once the appropriate space is set aside, utilize vertical space just as efficiently as floor space. Some washers and dryers are stackable, allowing smaller spaces to include folding tables or utility sinks. Install overhead cabinetry for storing laundry accessories from detergents to drying racks. At least 48 inches should be left in front of laundry units for easy movement and to provide extra space for future appliances to easily fit in the same location.

amenities

Today's laundry rooms are multi-taskers and often include home offices, crafting spaces, plant potting, or gift wrapping stations. The spaces are larger and include lots of built-in storage. Gone are the days of leaving the laundry room the minute the machine is started, now homeowners can work on their latest craft project while waiting for the towels to dry.

Another popular trend for mud rooms and laundry spaces is creating an accommodating spot for your furry family member. Homeowners are getting super creative when it comes to providing a comfortable environment for their pet. In fact, spending on our furry friends is steadily on the rise and that includes spending for their accommodations within the home, too. Have fun creating a built-in "crate," food and water dishes, or even a dog wash station. The possibilities are endless and not only add great function, but will look much more attractive than throwing a dog bed on the floor that everyone trips over.

Though laundry is not necessarily a fun task, the space itself does not need to be a drag. Today's appliances are sleeker than ever, coming in numerous shapes, sizes, and colors allowing you to customize your laundry room to match the rest of your home's decor. Reserve wall space for artwork and install attractive, yet functional flooring.

Though the average family does eight to ten loads of laundry per week, there is no reason it has to be overwhelming. Create a space equipped to tackle your family's needs, while including hobby and organization space, and suddenly the dreaded chore will feel less of a hassle and more of an escape to your happy place.

PLAN #904-139D-0068

Dimensions: 67'3" W x 89'9" D
Heated Sq. Ft.: 3,274
Bonus Sq. Ft.: 1,252
Bedrooms: 4   Bathrooms: 3½
Exterior Walls: 2" x 6"
Foundation: Crawl space standard;
slab, basement, daylight basement or
walk-out basement for an additional
fee

See index on page 104 for more information

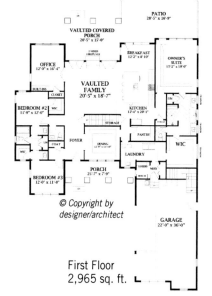
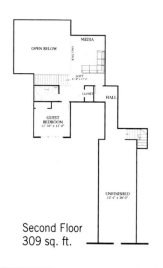

First Floor
2,965 sq. ft.

Second Floor
309 sq. ft.

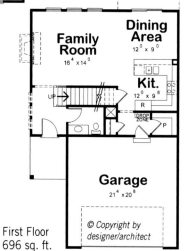

Second Floor
1,126 sq. ft.

PLAN #904-026D-2094

Dimensions: 29' W x 45' D
Heated Sq. Ft.: 1,822
Bedrooms: 3   Bathrooms: 2½
Foundation: Slab standard; crawl
space, basement or walk-out
basement for an additional fee

See index on page 104 for more information

First Floor
696 sq. ft.

CALL 1-800-373-2646   ONLINE houseplansandmore.com

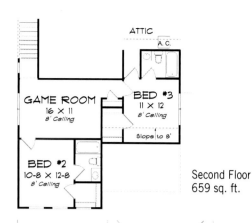

ATTIC

A.C.

GAME ROOM
16 X 11
8' Ceiling

BED #3
11 X 12
8' Ceiling

Slope to 8'

BED #2
10-8 X 12-8
8' Ceiling

Second Floor
659 sq. ft.

PLAN #904-130D-0387

Dimensions:	52' W x 44' D
Heated Sq. Ft.:	1,878
Bedrooms: 3	Bathrooms: 3½

Foundation: Slab standard; basement or crawl space for an additional fee

See index on page 104 for more information

Vault 9' to 12'

DINING ROOM
11 X 12
9' Ceiling

LIVING ROOM
16-4 X 19
12' Ceiling

Eating Bar

Side Pantry

GARAGE
20 X 22

Optional Basement Stairs

6' X 4' Island

© Copyright by designer/architect

Vault 9' to 12'

KIT
11 X 10

W.H.

BED #1
16 X 12
9' Ceiling

FOYER

W D

glass

ledge

PORCH
15-4 X 9

First Floor
1,219 sq. ft.

Images provided by designer/architect

PLAN #904-011D-0617

Dimensions:	69' W x 58' D
Heated Sq. Ft.:	2,104
Bonus Sq. Ft.:	268
Bedrooms: 3	Bathrooms: 2½
Exterior Walls:	2" x 6"

Foundation: Joisted continuous footings standard; basement for an additional fee

See index on page 104 for more information

DN

VAULTED
BONUS
11/6 X 19/4

Optional
Second Floor
268 sq. ft.

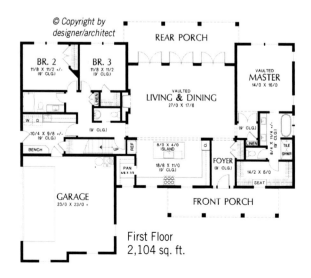

© Copyright by designer/architect

REAR PORCH

BR. 2
11/8 X 11/2 +/-
(9' CLG.)

BR. 3
11/8 X 11/2
(9' CLG.)

VAULTED
LIVING & DINING
27/0 X 17/6

VAULTED
MASTER
14/0 X 16/0

LINEN

10/4 X 9/8 +/-
(9' CLG.)

(9' CLG.)

8/0 X 4/0
ISLAND

LINEN

TILE

SHWR

BENCH

UP

REF

18/8 X 11/0
(9' CLG.)

FOYER
(9' CLG.)

14/2 X 5/0

PAN
4/8 X 1/2

GARAGE
23/0 X 23/0 +

SEAT

FRONT PORCH

First Floor
2,104 sq. ft.

PLAN #904-032D-0865

Dimensions: 44' W x 24' D
Heated Sq. Ft.: 1,587
Bedrooms: 3   Bathrooms: 2½
Exterior Walls: 2" x 6"
Foundation: Crawl space standard; basement, floating slab or monolithic slab for an additional fee
See index on page 104 for more information

© Copyright by designer/architect

11'-0" x 11'-8"   13'-8" x 14'-8"   12'-0" x 12'-4"

11'-2" x 11'-0"

First Floor
1,000 sq. ft.

11'-2" x 12'-0"   9'-6" x 12'-0"

6'-8" x 8'-0"

Second Floor
587 sq. ft.

PLAN #904-141D-0223

Dimensions: 52'10" W x 67'2" D
Heated Sq. Ft.: 2,095
Bedrooms: 3   Bathrooms: 2½
Exterior Walls: 2" x 6"
Foundation: Slab or crawl space, please specify when ordering
See index on page 104 for more information

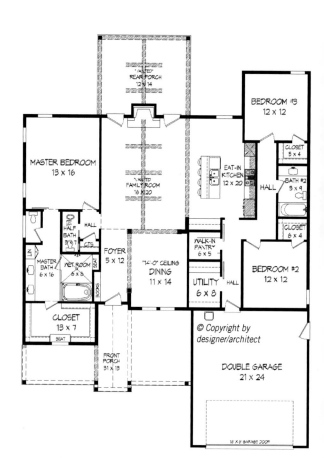

VAULTED REAR PORCH 12 x 14

MASTER BEDROOM 13 x 16

EAT-IN KITCHEN 12 x 20

BEDROOM #3 12 x 12

CLOSET 5 x 4

VAULTED FAMILY ROOM 16 x 20

HALL

BATH #2 5 x 9

HALF BATH

HALL

MASTER BATH 6 x 16

PET ROOM 6 x 6

FOYER 5 x 12

14'-0" CEILING DINING 11 x 14

WALK-IN PANTRY 6 x 5

CLOSET 6 x 4

UTILITY 6 x 8   HALL

BEDROOM #2 12 x 12

CLOSET 13 x 7

SEAT

© Copyright by designer/architect

FRONT PORCH 31 x 13

DOUBLE GARAGE 21 x 24

16 x 8 GARAGE DOOR

CALL 1-800-373-2646   **ONLINE** houseplansandmore.com

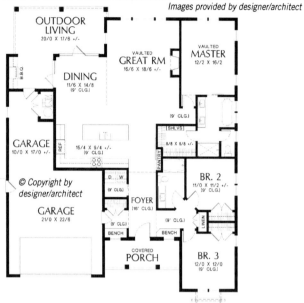

PLAN #904-011D-0627

Dimensions:	52' W x 61' D
Heated Sq. Ft.:	1,878
Bedrooms: 3	Bathrooms: 2
Exterior Walls:	2" x 6"

Foundation: Joisted crawl space
standard; slab for an additional fee

See index on page 104 for more information

PLAN #904-139D-0092

Dimensions:	73' W x 60'7" D
Heated Sq. Ft.:	2,966
Bonus Sq. Ft.:	808
Bedrooms: 3	Bathrooms: 2½
Exterior Walls:	2" x 6"

Foundation: Crawl space standard;
slab, basement, daylight basement or
walk-out basement for an additional
fee

See index on page 104 for more information

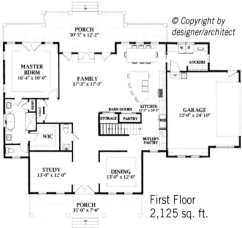

First Floor
2,125 sq. ft.

Second Floor
841 sq. ft.

PLAN #904-011S-0196

Dimensions:	144'6" W x 86' D
Heated Sq. Ft.:	7,149
Bedrooms: 4	Bathrooms: 4½
Exterior Walls:	2" x 6"

Foundation: Engineered joists with crawl space standard; slab or basement for an additional fee

See index on page 104 for more information

Images provided by designer/architect

SPECIAL FEATURES

- The elegant entrance of this luxurious home opens into a magnificent two-story great room
- Gain access to the second floor via one of two staircases - one has rear access to the guest bedroom, and the other is a dramatic curved stairway that opens into the balcony overlooking the great room and the secondary bedrooms and bath
- The master suite is in a wing to itself and offers a wonderful space to pamper yourself in comfort and relax in style
- Ample space to enjoy unwinding after a long day is provided by not only an outdoor kitchen but a golf simulator, game room, shop/hobby/training room and private pool bath
- 3-car side entry garage

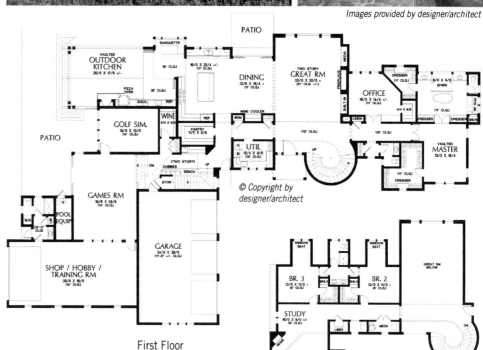

© Copyright by designer/architect

First Floor
5,355 sq. ft.

Second Floor
1,794 sq. ft.

PLAN #904-139D-0087

Dimensions: 76'10" W x 68'9" D
Heated Sq. Ft.: 3,409
Bonus Sq. Ft.: 332
Bedrooms: 4   Bathrooms: 3½
Exterior Walls: 2" x 6"
Foundation: Crawl space standard; slab, basement, daylight basement or walk-out basement for an additional fee

See index on page 104 for more information

First Floor
2,938 sq. ft.

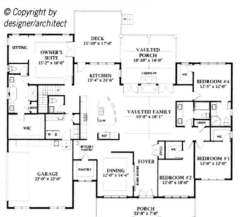

© Copyright by designer/architect

Second Floor
471 sq. ft.

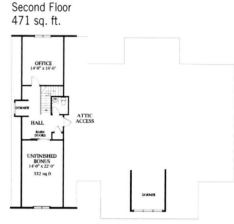

PLAN #904-051D-0980

Dimensions: 71' W x 53' D
Heated Sq. Ft.: 1,958
Bedrooms: 3   Bathrooms: 2
Exterior Walls: 2" x 6"
Foundation: Basement standard; crawl space or slab for an additional fee

See index on page 104 for more information

© Copyright by designer/architect

CALL 1-800-373-2646   ONLINE houseplansandmore.com

PLAN #904-011D-0653

Dimensions: 60' W x 53'6" D
Heated Sq. Ft.:   3,032
Bedrooms: 4   Bathrooms: 3½
Exterior Walls: 2" x 6"
Foundation: Joisted crawl space standard; basement for an additional fee

See index on page 104 for more information

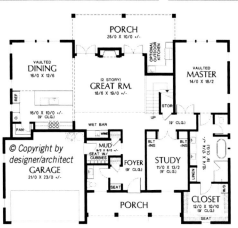

© Copyright by designer/architect

First Floor
1,959 sq. ft.

Second Floor
1,073 sq. ft.

© Copyright by designer/architect

First Floor
2,875 sq. ft.

PLAN #904-101D-0090

Dimensions: 78' W x 79' D
Heated Sq. Ft.:   2,875
Bonus Sq. Ft.:   1,611
Bedrooms: 3   Bathrooms: 3½
Exterior Walls: 2" x 6"
Foundation: Basement or daylight basement, please specify when ordering

See index on page 104 for more information

Images provided by designer/architect

Optional
Lower Level
1,611 sq. ft.

PLAN #904-167D-0008

Dimensions: 62'4" W x 50'7" D
Heated Sq. Ft.:   3,328
Bedrooms: 4   Bathrooms: 3½
Exterior Walls: 2" x 6"
Foundation: Crawl space standard;
slab for an additional fee
See index on page 104 for more information

FEATURES

- Inviting Modern Farmhouse has beamed ceilings and lots of windows creating a friendly and welcoming feel
- The large dining area handles entertaining without a hitch
- The kitchen has an island with dining space
- The first floor owner's suite has soaring ceilings, two walk-in closets, and private bath that rivals the most luxurious
- Off the kitchen you'll discover a mud room and a separate laundry room for complete organization
- Double doors lead to a private home office
- Enjoy outdoor gatherings on the covered porch or spacious deck
- 2-car side entry detached garage

Images provided by designer/architect

Second Floor
1,282 sq. ft.

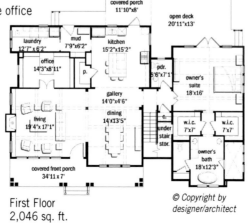

First Floor
2,046 sq. ft.

© Copyright by
designer/architect

CALL 1-800-373-2646   **ONLINE** houseplansandmore.com

PLAN #904-101D-0062

Dimensions:	87' W x 79'6" D
Heated Sq. Ft.:	2,648
Bonus Sq. Ft.:	1,799
Bedrooms: 3	Bathrooms: 3½
Exterior Walls:	2" x 6"

Foundation: Basement, daylight basement or walk-out basement, please specify when ordering

See index on page 104 for more information

Images provided by designer/architect

FEATURES

- Rustic charm enhances the curb appeal of this inviting family home
- Once inside, the great room, kitchen and dining area form the main gathering space
- The optional lower level has an additional 1,799 square feet of living area and includes a gym, a large recreation area with a half bath, and two additional bedrooms that share a bath
- 2-car side entry garage, and a 1-car front entry garage

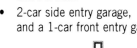

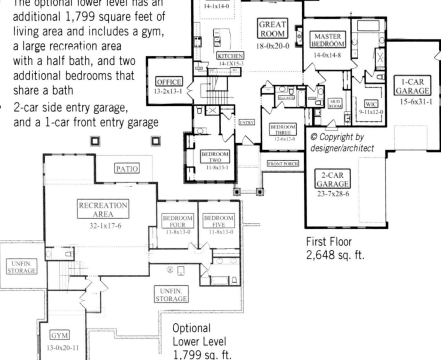

First Floor
2,648 sq. ft.

Optional
Lower Level
1,799 sq. ft.

© Copyright by designer/architect

PLAN #904-091D-0523

Dimensions:	69' W x 57'6" D
Heated Sq. Ft.:	2,514
Bonus Sq. Ft.:	390
Bedrooms: 4	Bathrooms: 3½
Exterior Walls:	2" x 6"

Foundation: Basement standard; crawl space or slab for an additional fee

See index on page 104 for more information

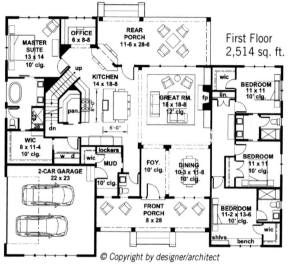

First Floor
2,514 sq. ft.

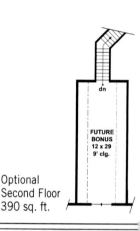

Optional
Second Floor
390 sq. ft.

© Copyright by designer/architect

PLAN #904-141D-0202

Dimensions:	81' W x 125'2" D
Heated Sq. Ft.:	5,317
Bedrooms: 5	Bathrooms: 4½

Foundation: Slab standard; crawl space, basement or walk-out basement for an additional fee

See index on page 104 for more information

© Copyright by designer/architect

First Floor
3,558 sq. ft.

Second Floor
1,759 sq. ft.

CALL 1-800-373-2646   **ONLINE** houseplansandmore.com

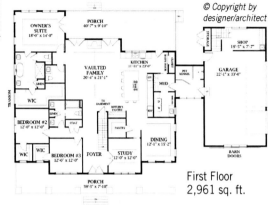

Second Floor
1,396 sq. ft.

PLAN #904-139D-0086

Dimensions:	92' W x 64'7" D
Heated Sq. Ft.:	4,357
Bonus Sq. Ft.:	579
Bedrooms: 5	Bathrooms: 4½
Exterior Walls:	2" x 6"

Images provided by designer/architect

Foundation: Crawl space standard; slab, basement, daylight basement or walk-out basement for an additional fee

See index on page 104 for more information

© Copyright by designer/architect

First Floor
2,961 sq. ft.

Images provided by designer/architect

PLAN #904-011D-0658

Dimensions:	50' W x 52' D
Heated Sq. Ft.:	2,618
Bedrooms: 4	Bathrooms: 2½
Exterior Walls:	2" x 6"

Foundation: Joisted crawl space standard; basement for an additional fee

See index on page 104 for more information

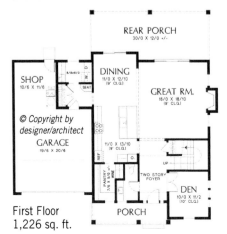

© Copyright by designer/architect

First Floor
1,226 sq. ft.

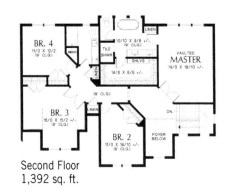

Second Floor
1,392 sq. ft.

PLAN #904-056D-0131

Dimensions: 80'10" W x 59' D
Heated Sq. Ft.: 3,154
Bonus Sq. Ft.: 269
Bedrooms: 5   Bathrooms: 3½
Foundation: Slab standard; crawl
space for an additional fee
See index on page 104 for more information

FEATURES

- With subtle Craftsman influences, this modern farmhouse style home has tremendous curb appeal with the wood accents and stonework
- Step inside from the covered porch and find a spacious and open vaulted lodge room with a window wall and a fireplace for a focal point
- Off the kitchen is a handy mud room that includes a powder room and a walk-in pantry
- The master bedroom enjoys its private location and has a private bath and massive walk-in closet
- The kitchen is positioned to overlook the lodge room and enjoys an oversized with dining space
- The vaulted outdoor covered porch is adorned with a fireplace allowing the homeowners to utilize this space long into the colder months of the year
- The optional bedroom on the second floor has an additional 269 square feet of living area
- 2-car side entry garage

First Floor
2,389 sq. ft.

© Copyright by
designer/architect

Second Floor
765 sq. ft.

Images provided by designer/architect

CALL 1-800-373-2646   **ONLINE** houseplansandmore.com

PLAN #904-155D-0128

Dimensions: 112' W x 71'2" D
Heated Sq. Ft.: 2,687
Bonus Sq. Ft.: 503
Bedrooms: 3   Bathrooms: 3
Exterior Walls: 2" x 6"
Foundation: Crawl space or slab
standard; basement or daylight
basement for an additional fee
See index on page 104 for more information

FEATURES

- Craftsman and Modern Farmhouse style collide in this two-story home featuring its own apartment garage perfect for an in-law suite, guest quarters, or rental space
- The huge covered front porch leads into the massively open great room with a large fireplace opposite the kitchen
- The kitchen enjoys having the dining table steps away and there's also a huge island with seating for five people
- The rear screened porch is a huge asset with an outdoor kitchen, a fireplace, and views of the backyard; this will be everyone's favorite spot
- The guest loft has an additional 503 square feet of living area and has a small kitchen, and a full bath with a double-bowl vanity and a large glass shower
- 2-car front entry garage attached via a breezeway

Second Floor
546 sq. ft.

© Copyright by
designer/architect

First Floor
2,141 sq. ft.

Images provided by designer/architect

PLAN #904-139D-0097

Dimensions:	69'8" W x 36'6" D
Heated Sq. Ft.:	2,715
Bonus Sq. Ft.:	315
Bedrooms: 3	Bathrooms: 3½
Exterior Walls:	2" x 6"

Foundation: Crawl space standard; slab, basement, daylight basement or walk-out basement for an additional fee

See index on page 104 for more information

First Floor 1,890 sq. ft.

Second Floor 825 sq. ft.

Second Floor 1,252 sq. ft.

PLAN #904-101D-0067

Dimensions:	54' W x 59' D
Heated Sq. Ft.:	2,726
Bonus Sq. Ft.:	1,074
Bedrooms: 4	Bathrooms: 2½
Exterior Walls:	2" x 6"
Foundation:	Basement

See index on page 104 for more information

Optional Lower Level 1,074 sq. ft.

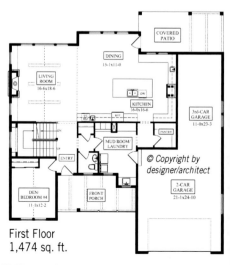

First Floor 1,474 sq. ft.

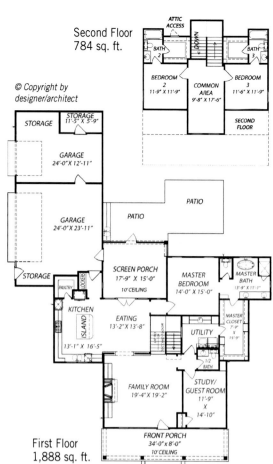

Second Floor
784 sq. ft.

© Copyright by
designer/architect

PLAN #904-170D-0003

Dimensions: 70'9" W x 91' D
Heated Sq. Ft.: 2,672
Bedrooms: 4   Bathrooms: 3½
Foundation: Slab standard; crawl
space, basement or daylight
basement for an additional fee
See index on page 104 for more information

Images provided by designer/architect

First Floor
1,888 sq. ft.

PLAN #904-052D-0171

Images provided by designer/architect

Dimensions: 88' W x 54' D
Heated Sq. Ft.: 3,562
Bonus Sq. Ft.: 1,899
Bedrooms: 5   Bathrooms: 4
Foundation: Walk-out basement
See index on page 104 for more information

Second Floor
1,463 sq. ft.

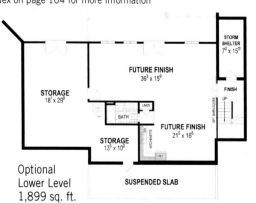

Optional
Lower Level
1,899 sq. ft.

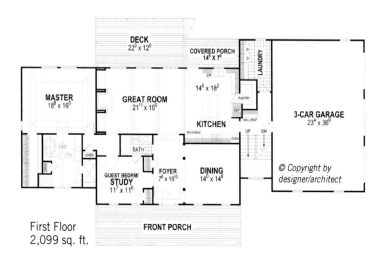

© Copyright by
designer/architect

First Floor
2,099 sq. ft.

beyond the grill:

take living
OUTDOORS

You wake to a perfectly sunny day. After a long stretch to awaken your senses you head to the French doors and swing them open to reveal an amazing oasis with stunning gardens, patios, and a waterfall. No, you are not on vacation – you are experiencing and living the luxury of your very own outdoor living area!

It seems homeowners have taken the idea of a "staycation" to a whole new level. Instead of jetting off to pricey tropical vacation destinations all the time, now more homeowners than ever are looking to invest their income into something more gratifying, their home. Why not invest in something you can truly enjoy every single day? Homeowners are enjoying staying at home more, and that includes entertaining on a more regular basis. With many home designs being designed smaller, more compact, and efficient, it seems only natural that entertaining and everyday living is now heading outdoors. The line between the interior spaces and the exterior ones has been blurred now more than ever before.

Both home and landscape designers have seen a huge desire by homeowners to bring an indoor entertainment experience to their outdoor spaces. By adding things like fireplaces, fire pits, outdoor kitchens, televisions, sound systems, etc., the party has definitely moved to the outdoors.

Think of your outdoor space as another room in your home. Gone are the days of rickety old rusted patio furniture and a wilted plant in one corner of the concrete slab patio. The best outdoor living areas rival the interior ones by creating an open flow that encourages easy entertaining, dining, and relaxing.

Do you love the idea of an outdoor kitchen? Then, make that one of the focal points. If your budget or area is small, maybe a deluxe grill is all you need to get the area ready for entertaining. Or, if you plan to spare no expense, then there are countless amenities available including: built-in grills, stovetops, refrigerators, and even a pizza oven can be a family fun spot that no doubt will be a conversation starter when friends are over for memorable get-togethers.

GET STARTED!
List some features you want to incorporate into your outdoor area so you can determine what the focal point should be.

There are two other popular features being added to outdoor spaces all across the country - one being a fire source, and the other being a water element. Both mesmerizing as well as relaxing, fire and water features are quickly gaining popularity in climates of all types. When it comes to fire, fire pits, outdoor fireplaces, and even barbecue grills fall into this popular category. Often evoking memories of childhood campfires and family time, adding a place where everyone can gather around a fire pit, or outdoor fireplace is bound to become a favorite backyard destination especially when the weather starts to cool down. This feature is an excellent way to extend your time in the outdoors earlier into the spring and later into the fall and early winter. Whether it's an intimate gathering with couples enjoying some wine on a fall evening, or a lively night with the entire family roasting marshmallows, one thing is for sure; a backyard fireplace or fire pit is bound to create countless memories.

Another focal point cropping up in outdoor spaces everywhere are water features. From waterfalls and fountains, to hot tubs and swimming pools, a water feature is a welcomed amenity that appeals to the senses. Nothing says refreshing like the cool, crystal blue waters of a swimming pool. And, the bubbling sound of a fountain or waterfall instantly refreshes and relaxes the soul. So, whatever your budget, there is a water solution for your outdoor space.

select a finish for your patio that mimics your interior flooring and instantly expand your living space visually. Homeowners are taking a lot of time and putting a lot of thought into treating and decorating outdoor patios like indoor rooms – again, bringing the look and feel of the home's interior to its outdoor spaces creates a cohesive experience between the indoors and the outdoors. While many homeowners may stick with traditional concrete or stamped concrete that comes in a variety of colors, what some designers believe is more aesthetically pleasing are pavers and flagstone products. These have also proven to be a wiser investment in terms of long term value and durability. So, start with the floor and select a beautiful foundation that mirrors your interior spaces. It will create a solid design anchor that will merge your indoor and outdoor rooms seamlessly. If your outdoor space is covered like many are today, you may even wish to use ceramic tile, or other stone tile surfaces that can be used both indoors and outdoors for the ultimate seamless look.

HOW DO YOU CREATE A SEAMLESS FEEL FROM YOUR OUTDOOR ROOM TO THE INDOOR SPACES OF YOUR HOME?

select furniture that resembles the interior style when it comes to colors and textures. This will further enhance the open feel of these merging spaces naturally and will keep the areas from looking disjointed. When investing in outdoor furniture, it is sometimes best to stick to neutral colors such as brown, beige, white, and other earth tones. These are timeless colors that make the perfect backdrop for highlighting outdoor artwork, textiles such as pillows, and other vividly colorful accessories. However, although neutral furniture is a wise investment, current trends in outdoor spaces show wildly bright and neon colored furniture gaining popularity. Regardless of its color, group furniture pieces creating several types of spaces for dining, intimate conversation spots, and seating areas for larger parties. If you have a special focal point in nature, don't forget to arrange a seating area so this can be enjoyed to its fullest. If you're lucky enough to have panoramic ocean or lake views, arrange one seating area so it completely enjoys this scenic vista with little or no visual distractions.

select color

including vibrant colors that have really made a comeback recently and add a tremendous amount of personality to any space both indoors and out. So, choose a few colors for your color scheme and have fun! Rich reds, bold oranges, vivid blues or garden-inspired greens all offer personality. Then, pair up some plants and flowers native to your area for easy maintenance. Select matching or contrasting colors and you'll have an outdoor area that exudes your own personal style.

HOT OR COLD?
What would you choose for your outdoor living area? Fire, water, or both? Why?

Last, don't forget to incorporate lighting that highlights all of the amazing features and design ideas you have added to your own outdoor paradise. Not only will "lightscaping" call attention to a focal point like a water feature, it can designate a space. For example, a chandelier or statement light fixture can spotlight a special dining spot, or a unique side table lamp will make an intimate outdoor space even more cozy and comfortable.

Don't let another season go by without finding a way to smoothly transition your indoor and outdoor spaces into something truly spectacular. Use some or all of these great outdoor design trends to provide a year-round outdoor oasis that creates a sanctuary for your senses just steps from your home's interior.

PLAN #904-026D-1913

Dimensions: 34' W x 60'4" D
Heated Sq. Ft.: 3,322
Bedrooms: 6 Bathrooms: 3½
Exterior Walls: 2" x 6"
Foundation: Basement standard;
walk-out basement for an additional fee
See index on page 104 for more information

FEATURES

- The two-story living room is open and brings in the outdoors with its large windows
- The optional lower level has a family room, two bedrooms, and a bath making it a private living space, and there's space for storage
- The laundry room is centrally located on the second floor
- 3-car rear entry garage

Second Floor
1,345 sq. ft.

Lower Level
806 sq. ft.

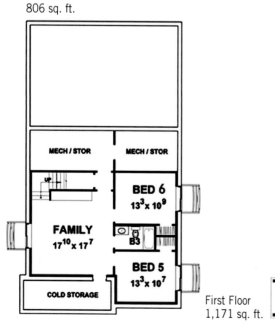

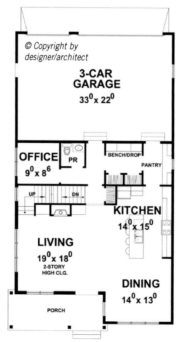

First Floor
1,171 sq. ft.

Images provided by designer/architect

CALL 1-800-373-2646   **ONLINE** houseplansandmore.com

PLAN #904-101D-0065

Dimensions:	65' W x 76'6" D
Heated Sq. Ft.:	2,269
Bonus Sq. Ft.:	1,563
Bedrooms: 2	Bathrooms: 2½
Exterior Walls:	2" x 6"
Foundation:	Basement

See index on page 104 for more information

FEATURES

- Come on in to this stylish farmhouse inspired home and be awed by the unique free-standing fireplace that is a focal point in the great room
- The open kitchen features an oversized island with enough space for dining and prepping meals and also a walk-in pantry
- The master bedroom enjoys a private location and features a luxury bath with a walk-in closet
- The oversized mudroom has a built-in bench and plenty of storage
- A handy elevator connects the first floor and lower level effortlessly making it possible to use one of the lower level bedrooms as an in-law suite
- The optional lower level has an additional 1,563 square feet of living area including a large living room, and two additional bedrooms each with their own bath
- 3-car front entry garage

First Floor
2,269 sq. ft.

© Copyright by designer/architect

Optional
Lower Level
1,563 sq. ft.

Images provided by designer/architect

PLAN #904-032D-1034

Dimensions: 70' W x 54' D
Heated Sq. Ft.: 3,164
Bedrooms: 4   Bathrooms: 3½
Exterior Walls: 2" x 6"
Foundation: Crawl space or basement standard; floating slab or monolithic slab for an additional fee
See index on page 104 for more information

© Copyright by designer/architect

First Floor
2,136 sq. ft.

Second Floor
1,028 sq. ft.

PLAN #904-051D-0978

Dimensions: 47' W x 54' D
Heated Sq. Ft.: 1,871
Bedrooms: 2   Bathrooms: 2
Exterior Walls: 2" x 6"
Foundation: Slab
See index on page 104 for more information

First Floor
1,080 sq. ft.

© Copyright by designer/architect

Second Floor
791 sq. ft.

CALL 1-800-373-2646   **ONLINE** houseplansandmore.com

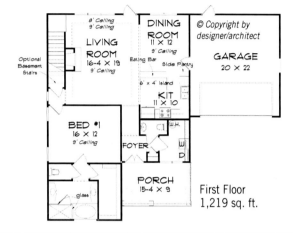

Second Floor
918 sq. ft.

First Floor
1,219 sq. ft.

Images provided by designer/architect

PLAN #904-130D-0389

Dimensions: 52' W x 44' D
Heated Sq. Ft.: 2,137
Bedrooms: 4   Bathrooms: 4½
Foundation: Slab standard; basement
or crawl space for an additional fee

See index on page 104 for more information

Images provided by designer/architect

PLAN #904-139D-0094

Dimensions: 67'7" W x 65'5" D
Heated Sq. Ft.: 2,915
Bonus Sq. Ft.: 856
Bedrooms: 3   Bathrooms: 3½
Exterior Walls: 2" x 6"
Foundation: Crawl space standard;
slab, basement, daylight basement or
walk-out basement for an additional
fee

See index on page 104 for more information

First Floor
1,782 sq. ft.

Second Floor
1,133 sq. ft.

PLAN #904-076D-0220

Dimensions: 97'2" W x 87'7" D
Heated Sq. Ft.:   3,061
Bonus Sq. Ft.:   3,644
Bedrooms: 3   Bathrooms: 3½
Foundation: Basement, crawl space
or slab, please specify when ordering
See index on page 104 for more information

Images provided by designer/architect

FEATURES

- This luxury Craftsman home is loaded with curb appeal thanks to multiple gables, and a covered porch adding that undeniable charm

- The first floor is open and airy with the main gathering spaces combining perfectly maximizing the square footage

- The kitchen is open to the family room with a grilling terrace nearby

- The optional lower level has an additional 2,975 square feet of living area including a hobby room, theater, office, and a recreation area with a bar

- The optional second floor has an additional 669 square feet of living area with 277 square feet in the bedroom and 392 square feet in the recreation area

- 3-car front entry garage

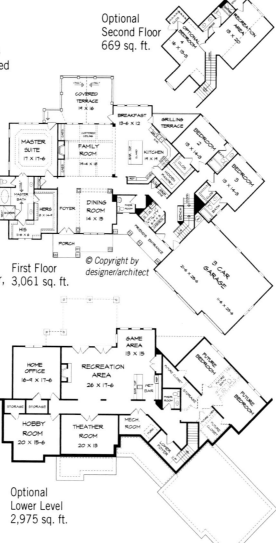

Optional
Second Floor
669 sq. ft.

First Floor
3,061 sq. ft.

© Copyright by
designer/architect

Optional
Lower Level
2,975 sq. ft.

Images provided by designer/architect

PLAN #904-032D-1104

Dimensions: 32' W x 30' D
Heated Sq. Ft.:   1,920
Bedrooms: 3   Bathrooms: 2
Exterior Walls: 2" x 6"
Foundation: Basement standard;
crawl space for an additional fee
See index on page 104 for more information

FEATURES

- This charming design has all of the modern farmhouse style you desire and with the open concept layout homeowners want today
- The kitchen features a large island and it overlooks the main living area with patio access
- An oversized walk-in pantry keeps the kitchen neat and organized
- The master bedroom features a walk-in closet and enjoys the luxury of the first floor bath with free-standing tub and separate shower
- The lower level has a spacious laundry room with a laundry chute for ease with this household chore
- A spacious family room, two additional bedrooms and a bath complete this comfortable home

© Copyright by designer/architect

First floor
960 sq. ft.

Lower level
960 sq. ft.

Second Floor
713 sq. ft.

PLAN #904-011D-0622

Dimensions: 46' W x 79' D
Heated Sq. Ft.: 2,490
Bedrooms: 3   Bathrooms: 2½
Exterior Walls: 2" x 6"
Foundation: Joisted continuous footings standard; slab or basement for an additional fee

See index on page 104 for more information

Images provided by designer/architect

© Copyright by
designer/architect

First Floor
1,777 sq. ft.

Images provided by designer/architect

PLAN #904-077D-0293

Dimensions: 58' W x 58'6" D
Heated Sq. Ft.: 1,800
Bedrooms: 3   Bathrooms: 2
Foundation: Slab or crawl space, please specify when ordering

See index on page 104 for more information

    CALL 1-800-373-2646   **ONLINE** houseplansandmore.com

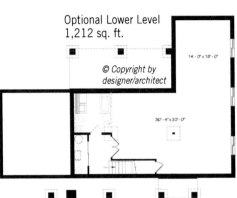

PLAN #904-032D-0971

Dimensions:	60' W x 40' D
Heated Sq. Ft.:	1,212
Bonus Sq. Ft.:	1,212
Bedrooms: 2	Bathrooms: 1
Exterior Walls:	2" x 6"

Foundation: Basement standard; crawl space, monolithic slab, floating slab or walk-out basement for an additional fee

See index on page 104 for more information

Optional Lower Level
1,212 sq. ft.

© Copyright by designer/architect

14' - 0" x 18' - 0"

50' - 4" x 20' - 0"

First Floor
1,212 sq. ft.

COVERED PORCH / OUTDOOR KITCHEN
26 - 0 X 18 - 0

BEDROOM 1
14-9 X 15-0

1-CAR GARAGE
17-3 X 20-9

MAIN AREA
26 - 1 X 20-9
EXPOSED BEAM

BATHROOM

BEDROOM 2
9-8 X 10-6

KITCHEN

FOYER

COVERED PORCH

PLAN #904-121D-0039

Dimensions:	61' W x 40'4" D
Heated Sq. Ft.:	1,624
Bedrooms: 3	Bathrooms: 2

Foundation: Basement standard; crawl space or slab for an additional fee

See index on page 104 for more information

MBr
14-9x17-6
Std Vault Clg
Opt Coffer Clg

Br 2
10-6x11-11

Kitchen/ Brkfst
17-8x15-10

Dn

Porch

Garage
21-4x21-6

Br 3
11-2x11-10

Foyer

Great Rm
15-4x18-6

Porch

© Copyright by designer/architect

PLAN #904-101D-0094

Dimensions:	72' W x 72'9" D
Heated Sq. Ft.:	2,650
Bonus Sq. Ft.:	1,821
Bedrooms: 3	Bathrooms: 2½
Exterior Walls:	2" x 6"
Foundation:	Basement

See index on page 104 for more information

Images provided by designer/architect

FEATURES

- Sleek Prairie-inspired exterior is refreshing and uncomplicated creating great curb appeal
- The dining area, kitchen and great room combine creating a large informal gathering space for family and friends to relax
- A U-shaped layout and curved breakfast bar highlight the kitchen
- Located right off the garage is a mud room, laundry room and walk-in pantry
- With double walk-in closets, a luxurious bath complete with a free-standing tub and see-through fireplace, this master suite is the perfect retreat
- The optional lower level has an additional 1,821 square feet of living area and includes a large recreation room with a wet bar, two additional bedrooms and a full bath, plus a wine room
- 3-car front entry garage

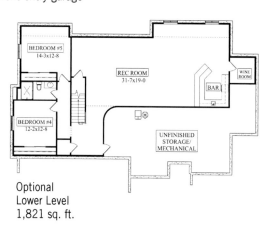

Optional
Lower Level
1,821 sq. ft.

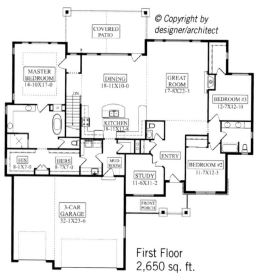

© Copyright by
designer/architect

First Floor
2,650 sq. ft.

CALL 1-800-373-2646   **ONLINE** houseplansandmore.com

PLAN #904-028D-0099

Dimensions:	30' W x 49' D
Heated Sq. Ft.:	1,320
Bedrooms: 3	Bathrooms: 2
Exterior Walls:	2" x 6"
Foundation:	Monolithic slab

See index on page 104 for more information

Images provided by designer/architect

FEATURES

- In a sensible size, this cottage can easily incorporate popular Modern Farmhouse style trends into its floor plan with a barn style door from the master bedroom into the bath and rustic floating shelves for storage in the kitchen
- The great room and kitchen/dining area blend together making the interior feel larger than its true size
- Three bedrooms are located near each other for convenience
- A laundry room is centrally located adding ease with this chore

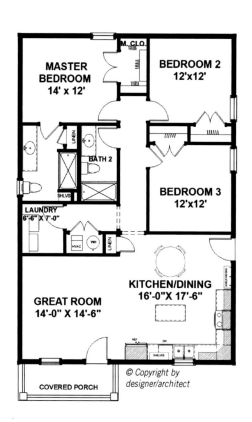

MASTER BEDROOM 14' x 12'

M. CLO.

BEDROOM 2 12'x12'

LINEN

BATH 2

SHLVS

LAUNDRY 6'-6" X 7'-0"

HVAC WH LINEN

BEDROOM 3 12'x12'

GREAT ROOM 14'-0" X 14'-6"

KITCHEN/DINING 16'-0"X 17'-6"

REF DW SHELVES

COVERED PORCH

© Copyright by designer/architect

PLAN #904-101D-0087

Dimensions:	79'6" W x 71' D
Heated Sq. Ft.:	3,880
Bonus Sq. Ft.:	1,258
Bedrooms: 3	Bathrooms: 3½
Exterior Walls:	2" x 6"

Foundation: Basement or daylight basement, please specify when ordering

See index on page 104 for more information

FEATURES

Images provided by designer/architect

- This whimsical Craftsman farmhouse has an exterior with major curb appeal thanks to the covered front porch and unique window sizes and arrangements

- The expansive living room is topped with a beamed ceiling and flows directly into the kitchen and dining area for a more open feel

- A large combination mud room/laundry area has built-in lockers, plenty of storage, and a sink

- The second floor features a vaulted master bedroom with two walk-in closets and a posh bath, a study, a bedroom with bath and plenty of storage space

- The optional lower level has an additional 1,258 square feet of living area including a rec room with a fireplace, and two additional bedrooms that share a full bath

- 2-car front entry garage, and a 2-car front entry tandem garage

Second Floor
1,778 sq. ft.

© Copyright by designer/architect

First Floor
2,102 sq. ft.

Optional
Lower Level
1,258 sq. ft.

PLAN #904-011D-0660

Dimensions: 52' W x 53' D
Heated Sq. Ft.: 1,704
Bedrooms: 3   Bathrooms: 2½
Exterior Walls: 2" x 6"
Foundation: Joisted continuous footings or post & beam standard; slab for an additional fee

See index on page 104 for more information

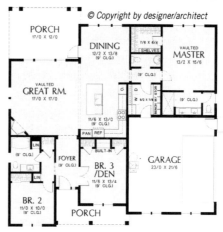

© Copyright by designer/architect

PLAN #904-101D-0068

Dimensions: 71'6" W x 64' D
Heated Sq. Ft.: 3,231
Bonus Sq. Ft.: 368
Bedrooms: 4   Bathrooms: 2½
Exterior Walls: 2" x 6"
Foundation: Basement

See index on page 104 for more information

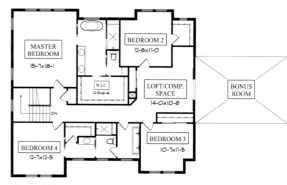

Second Floor
1,612 sq. ft.

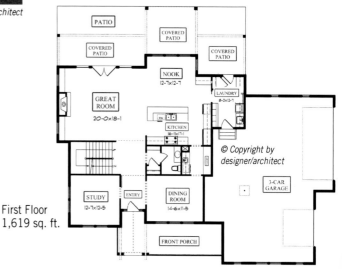

First Floor
1,619 sq. ft.

© Copyright by designer/architect

CALL 1-800-373-2646   **ONLINE** houseplansandmore.com

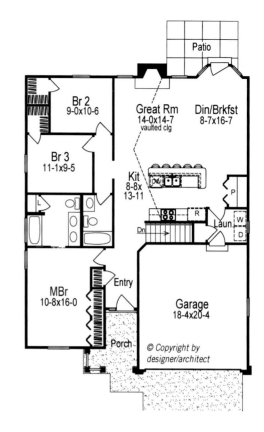

PLAN #904-007D-5060

Dimensions: 36' W x 46'4" D
Heated Sq. Ft.: 1,344
Bedrooms: 3   Bathrooms: 2
Foundation: Basement standard; crawl space or slab for an additional fee

See index on page 104 for more information

Images provided by designer/architect

PLAN #904-167D-0006

Dimensions: 68'11" W x 69'10" D
Heated Sq. Ft.: 2,939
Bedrooms: 4   Bathrooms: 3½
Exterior Walls: 2" x 6"
Foundation: Slab standard; crawl space for an additional fee

See index on page 104 for more information

Images provided by designer/architect

the SOCIAL KITCHEN

You just put the finishing touches on a beautiful table centerpiece, a spread of hors d'oeuvres, and other culinary treats for your gathering. Every attention to detail has been made to the great room, dining area, and the gathering places in your home. You want to make sure your guests feel pampered, comfortable, and completely at ease. But, no matter how inviting your great room may be, why does it always seem everyone ends up in the kitchen?

Kitchens are magnets for everyone who enters a home. Maybe it's the flurry of activity taking place there, or the scrumptious aromas that fill the air making guests want to investigate what possibly could be cooking. Whatever the reason, kitchens are everyone's go-to gathering spot. So, instead of fighting it, make your kitchen socially inviting and a place that's comfortable and fun, while still allowing you to get things done even if people are lingering about. There are many ways to create social spots in the kitchen, that allow guests to feel welcome.

Thankfully, today's floor plans are embracing this common occurrence now more than ever. Homes being designed today utilize an open floor plan that easily integrates the kitchen into the surrounding gathering spaces seamlessly. So, the kitchen is no longer hidden behind a swinging door. It's actually a stunning focal point filled with many design elements that enhance the entire gathering area including seating, dining space, and other functional amenities.

The kitchen is the center of your home; where you do the most work, where you entertain friends, where you gather as a family, and where life happens. It is hands-down the busiest area of the home and needs to be carefully planned for function as well as style.

But, a home's kitchen tends to be a place that turns into a dumping ground. With the daily mail, homework projects, laundry, food storage, and office work finding its way there, the kitchen often has an identity crisis since there are so many different activities being carried out in the same space. Well, these habits will never change most likely, so instead of letting them aggravate you, embrace them and learn how to incorporate all of your family's favorite activities into this one wonderful place.

One way to create an inviting place with function within your kitchen is to create a chopping and chatting spot. Whether it's a breakfast bar counter, an island, workbench or table, guests and family need a spot that functions as a place for dining, prepping a meal, or finishing homework due tomorrow. A decent space for gathering around will become a beacon and will keep everyone right where the action is, but out of the cooking area. An important thing to remember when creating this gathering spot is that you don't want to crowd your kitchen with too many tables, or an island that is too oversized. It shouldn't affect the natural traffic flow, or act as a barrier. Pick a piece of furniture, or a space that facilitates function, storage, and possibly workspace, plus a spot where people can just hang out and not be in the chef's way.

Another important factor to include when creating a social kitchen is to make sure there's plenty of seating. Use stools, benches and other seating options to offer places for your guests to hang out. Of course, you may be thinking that your dining table has chairs and that should be enough, but think of additional types of seating that can be tucked away (under a counter, for example) and remain out of sight. Benches are great because they provide a handy place to drop things the minute you come in the door, plus when company arrive, it's a spot for chatting with the cook. Everyone enjoys gathering in the kitchen and having chips and dip, while watching the cook finish up meal time tasks. Having comfortable seating options ensures your guests are comfortable and at ease instead of standing around. Even better, stick with wood, plastic or other low-maintenance options and if spills occur, clean up will be a breeze.

Adding a variety of lighting in the kitchen is another way to make this space feel inviting, warm and comfortable for everyone. Add under the cabinet lights, recessed lighting, a statement light over the table, and additional lighting in work zones so that all of the bases are covered. That way, when the family cozies up around the table playing games after dinner, you can adjust the light to illuminate only the table area.

Use soft light when entertaining, and then when cooking or prepping, turn up the lights so it's safer. Even soft candlelight adds warmth and dimension to a space making it feel intimate and less institutional. An inexpensive way to change the amount of light in your kitchen is to install dimmer switches. That way, the light above the sink can be bright enough for kitchen tasks at mealtime and then turned down lower and used as a night light after everyone has gone to bed. Dimmers allow versatility and keep your kitchen from being too bright, which also saves electricity.

Making some minor adjustments with the layout, seating options, and lighting can score points when family and guests gather in your kitchen. Instead of trying to find ways to keep everyone out while you cook away, invite them in and let the party begin the minute they arrive.

your dream kitchen wish list

If you're designing the ultimate kitchen, working to make your kitchen more functional, or building a new home and trying to remember everything for the ultimate kitchen layout, it is important to remember that the kitchen is one of the smartest places to invest your money when building so make sure it meets all of your needs right from the start.

The three main appliances in the kitchen are the sink, the refrigerator, and the stove. Make sure you arrange them so the workspace flows.

SINK OR SWIM
Of the three appliances, the sink gets the most use. Place it in an area of the kitchen that is visually appealing to its user. So, don't push it up against a wall without a view. Place it in front of a window with a view outdoors, or in an island that overlooks other spaces in the home. It is also important to place the dishwasher on either side of the sink so that loading dishes is convenient. Many kitchens have a second sink, one for preparing food, or another for dishes. Some kitchens also feature a second dishwasher, one for gently washing breakables and another for power scrubbing pots and pans.

SHUT THE FRIDGE
When it comes to the refrigerator there are many options such as brand, color, size and finish. But, also think about the various styles including a freezer/fridge combination, side-by-side doors, a top and bottom door style, a style with an ice and water dispenser in the door, a smart fridge with technology that allows you to see what's inside it from your smart phone, and now there are fun retro refrigerators meant to make a bold decorating statement and focal point. Also showing resurgence, refrigerators with doors having the look as the cabinets so it doesn't stand out. Shiny stainless steel finishes are becoming less popular as the new appliances being introduced have a more matte finish. Whatever option you choose make sure you leave plenty of room for the doors to open completely. If the fridge is placed near a wall make sure the doors and drawers open freely without hitting the wall. It is a good idea to check with the manufacturer for specific installation dimensions. Also becoming extremely popular are the counter depth refrigerators especially when a kitchen is small. These slightly smaller sized models offer a seamless look that feels custom since the appliance doesn't stick out further than the countertops. It easily adds square footage to your kitchen without it being obvious.

TOO HOT IN THE KITCHEN
The options available for stoves go way beyond gas or electric. There are cooktops, double ovens, oven and microwave combinations, burners and griddle tops, convection and even warming drawers. When making a decision it is important to think about the type of cooking you plan to do and how much space you have to work with. The cooking surface needs to be planned to allow for workspace that is easily accessible and safe. Many ovens and stoves are now smart device friendly allowing you to turn them on and off remotely.

The selection process isn't over just yet. It's time to think about cabinets, shelving, countertops, pantries, closets, a planning center, electronics, a center island, and eating space!

CABINETS, SHELVING & COUNTERTOPS
You can never have too much storage and this is especially true in the kitchen with all of the gadgets to be stored. Most common are cabinets with closed fronts, but open cabinets where plates are stored on end and open shelving where objects are quickly within reach are gaining popularity. It's a good idea to consider cabinets that go to the ceiling. The top shelf can be reached with a step stool and can hold items not used daily. Countertops need to be durable and can

include built-in items such as cutting boards and sinks. There are many surfaces available, so the biggest decision is how long you want it to last and how much you want to spend. Granite has long been a favorite, but homeowners are opting for quartz, concrete, or recycled glass, too.

PANTRIES, STORAGE WALLS & CLOSETS
Pantries are great for storing all food in one place. They are wider than a standard cabinet and have storage shelves. If space allows, a walk-in pantry closet is a great addition to a kitchen. They can be placed in the general vicinity of the kitchen with shelving added for your specific storage needs. Storage walls in kitchens are very popular too, and typically located near the stove. Shelves are mounted on a wall near the stove and include spices, measuring cups, oils, vinegars and other cooking essentials. Or, kitchen storage walls are often floor-to-ceiling and have an assortment of china, ceramic bowls, glassware and other items that look nice displayed together.

PLANNING & TECHNOLOGY CENTERS

Growing in popularity, the planning or technology center is basically a simplified "home office" located in the kitchen or adjacent to it. It can consist of a desk with surrounding cabinets and storage, space for a computer or iPad®, a charging station with additional USB ports, an area to organize bills and other important papers, cubbies or bins for every family member to stay organized, and a family schedule.

KITCHEN ELECTRONICS

There are so many items that are used in the kitchen that need to be plugged in, make sure there are plenty of electrical outlets so you don't have to run extension cords. Mockett® simplifies the need for electrical outlets everywhere in the kitchen with the pop-up kitchen outlet design (see right). Simply, click it and it ascends from the countertops to reveal additional outlets that can be used when additional seldom used appliances are needed.

KITCHEN ISLANDS

An island in the kitchen can function as an eating bar, additional workspace, or can house the cooktop or sink. Whatever the function, it usually ends up being the focal point of the kitchen and can be accented with dramatic lighting, or hanging kitchen racks that will creatively hold your pots and pans while reclaiming valuable cabinet space. Designing it with different colors than the other cabinets and countertops is a popular trend and makes it even more of a focal point.

EATING SPACE

This can be a nook, breakfast bar, banquette or island and for many families on the go it is where most of the meals are served. If you plan on having an eat-in kitchen, make sure there is enough stools so everyone has a place to sit.

If you're trying to design or plan the layout of a new kitchen the options are a little overwhelming, but it is important to remember that it needs to be well-organized and efficient, as well as beautiful since it is everyone's favorite spot. After all, it is the place you live, entertain and most importantly – cook! From cabinetry to appliances, it is important to create the perfect gathering space so that the chef, as well as family and friends, are always happy when they enter.

Images provided by designer/architect

Images provided by designer/architect

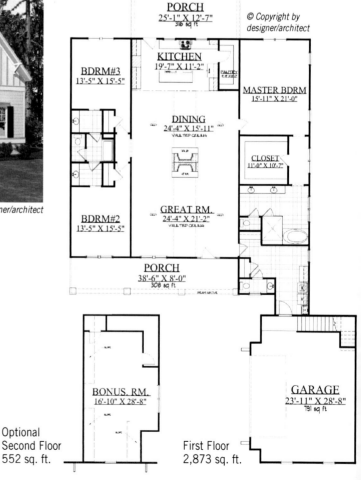

PLAN #904-028D-0100

Dimensions: 46' W x 42'6" D
Heated Sq. Ft.: 1,311
Bedrooms: 3   Bathrooms: 2
Exterior Walls: 2" x 6"
Foundation: Crawl space standard;
slab for an additional fee
See index on page 104 for more information

PLAN #904-157D-0023

Dimensions: 65'11 W x 107' D
Heated Sq. Ft.: 2,873
Bonus Sq. Ft.: 552
Bedrooms: 3   Bathrooms: 2½
Foundation: Crawl space standard;
slab for an additional fee
See index on page 104 for more information

CALL 1-800-373-2646   ONLINE houseplansandmore.com

PLAN #904-026D-2092

Dimensions: 45' W x 59'8" D
Heated Sq. Ft.: 2,448
Bedrooms: 4   Bathrooms: 3½
Foundation: Basement standard;
crawl space or slab for an additional fee

See index on page 104 for more information

Images provided by designer/architect

Owner's Suite
16⁴ x 14⁰
10'-0" CEILING

Br.3
11⁰ x 11⁸

Br.4
11⁸ x 12⁴

Br.2
12⁴ x 12⁴

Second Floor
1,336 sq. ft.

Family Room
16⁴ x 18⁶

Dining Area
10⁰ x 11⁸

Kit.
12⁴ x 12⁹

PATIO

Garage
21⁸ x 23¹⁰/33⁸

Flex Room
12² x 10⁴

© Copyright by designer/architect

First Floor
1,112 sq. ft.

COVERED PORCH

PLAN #904-077D-0019

Dimensions: 54' W x 47' D
Heated Sq. Ft.: 1,400
Bedrooms: 3   Bathrooms: 2
Foundation: Slab, crawl space or basement, please specify when ordering

See index on page 104 for more information

Images provided by designer/architect

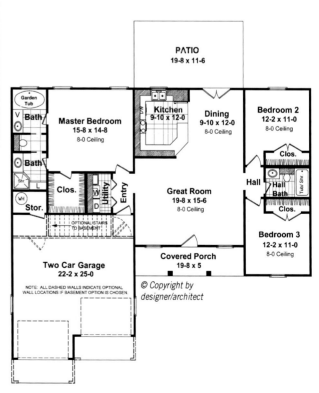

PATIO
19-8 x 11-6

Garden Tub

Bath

Bath

Master Bedroom
15-8 x 14-8
8-0 Ceiling

Kitchen
9-10 x 12-0

Dining
9-10 x 12-0
8-0 Ceiling

Bedroom 2
12-2 x 11-0
8-0 Ceiling

Clos.

Clos.

Utility

Entry

Great Room
19-8 x 15-6
8-0 Ceiling

Hall

Hall Bath

WH

Stor.

OPTIONAL STAIRS TO BASEMENT

Two Car Garage
22-2 x 25-0

Covered Porch
19-8 x 5

Bedroom 3
12-2 x 11-0
8-0 Ceiling

NOTE: ALL DASHED WALLS INDICATE OPTIONAL WALL LOCATIONS IF BASEMENT OPTION IS CHOSEN.

© Copyright by designer/architect

PLAN #904-101D-0050

Dimensions: 110'6" W x 84' D
Heated Sq. Ft.:   4,784
Bonus Sq. Ft.:   1,926
Bedrooms: 5   Bathrooms: 4½
Exterior Walls: 2" x 6"
Foundation: Walk-out basement

See index on page 104 for more information

Images provided by designer/architect

FEATURES

- Rustic beams above the entry give this home a lodge feel

- The first floor enjoys an open floor plan that has the kitchen in the center of activity surrounded by the great room and casual dining area both featuring fireplaces

- The private master bedroom and bath enjoy covered deck access and double walk-in closets

- A quiet home office is hidden behind the kitchen

- The second floor loft is a nice place to hang-out, and the laundry room is located near the second floor bedrooms for ease with this frequent chore

- The optional lower level has an additional 1,926 square feet of living area and enjoys a wet bar and family room for entertaining, and for hobbies there's a climbing room and craft room

- 2-car side entry garage, and a 1-car front entry garage

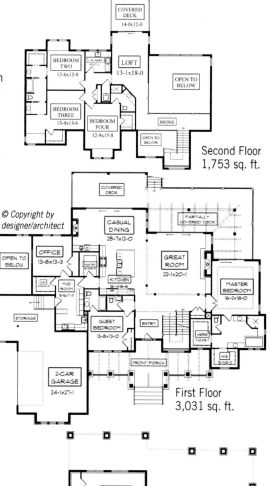

Second Floor
1,753 sq. ft.

© Copyright by designer/architect

First Floor
3,031 sq. ft.

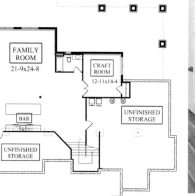

Optional
Lower Level
1,926 sq. ft.

CALL 1-800-373-2646   **ONLINE** houseplansandmore.com

PLAN #904-101D-0088

Dimensions:	69'6" W x 83' D
Heated Sq. Ft.:	2,442
Bonus Sq. Ft.:	1,977
Bedrooms: 2	Bathrooms: 2½
Exterior Walls:	2" x 6"
Foundation:	Basement

See index on page 104 for more information

FEATURES

- This beautiful home maximizes its square footage by combining all gathering spaces into one
- The private master bedroom enjoys a huge bath with a glass walk-in shower and a walk-in closet
- A large mud room has built-in lockers and an enormous walk-in closet for storage
- An office can be found behind the double doors off of the front entry
- The optional lower level has an additional 1,977 square feet of living area including a large rec room with a huge wrap-around countered wet bar, a media area, an exercise room, and two additional bedrooms that share a Jack and Jill bath
- 3-car front entry garage

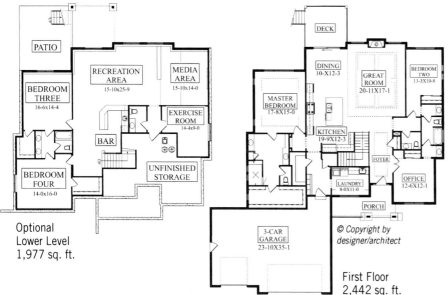

Optional Lower Level
1,977 sq. ft.

First Floor
2,442 sq. ft.

© Copyright by designer/architect

Images provided by designer/architect

Images provided by designer/architect

PLAN #904-056D-0104

Dimensions: 63'1" W x 41'10" D
Heated Sq. Ft.:   1,925
Bedrooms: 3   Bathrooms: 2½
Foundation: Slab
See index on page 104 for more information

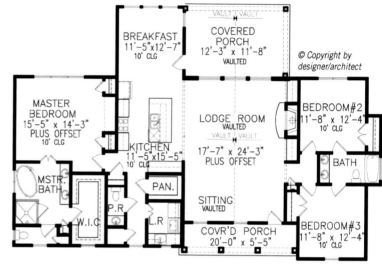

© Copyright by designer/architect

PLAN #904-155D-0110

Dimensions: 70' W x 63'2" D
Heated Sq. Ft.:   2,711
Bonus Sq. Ft.:   828
Bedrooms: 3   Bathrooms: 2½
Exterior Walls: 2" x 6"
Foundation: Crawl space or slab
standard; daylight basement or
basement for an additional fee
See index on page 104 for more information

Images provided by designer/architect

© Copyright by designer/architect

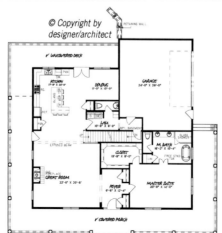

First Floor
2,005 sq. ft.

Second Floor
706 sq. ft.

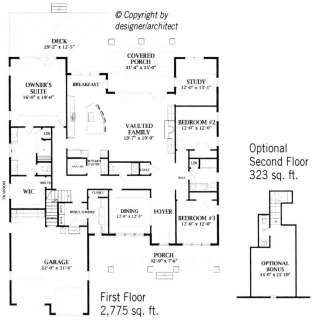

© Copyright by designer/architect

PLAN #904-139D-0059

Dimensions: 61'3" W x 85'5" D
Heated Sq. Ft.: 2,775
Bonus Sq. Ft.: 323
Bedrooms: 3   Bathrooms: 2½
Exterior Walls: 2" x 6"
Foundation: Crawl space standard; slab, basement, daylight basement or walk-out basement for an additional fee

See index on page 104 for more information

DECK 29'-2" x 12'-5"

COVERED PORCH 31'-4" x 15'-0"

STUDY 12'-0" x 13'-1"

OWNER'S SUITE 16'-0" x 19'-0"

BREAKFAST

VAULTED FAMILY 19'-7" x 19'-0"

BEDROOM #2 12'-0" x 12'-0"

LIN

BUTLER'S PANTRY

PANTRY

COAT

LIN

HALL

WIC

SHELVES

CLOSET

MUD/LAUNDRY

DINING 12'-0" x 12'-3"

FOYER

BEDROOM #3 12'-0" x 12'-0"

GARAGE 22'-0" x 21'-6"

PORCH 32'-9" x 7'-6"

First Floor
2,775 sq. ft.

Optional Second Floor
323 sq. ft.

OPTIONAL BONUS 14'-0" x 21'-10"

PLAN #904-101D-0076

Dimensions: 66'6" W x 80' D
Heated Sq. Ft.: 2,491
Bonus Sq. Ft.: 1,584
Bedrooms: 3   Bathrooms: 2½
Exterior Walls: 2" x 6"
Foundation: Basement or daylight basement, please specify when ordering

See index on page 104 for more information

MASTER BEDROOM 16-10x15-1

DINING 13-6x12-2

COVERED DECK

COVERED DECK

GREAT ROOM 20-0x16-0

BEDROOM TWO 15-0x14-2

1-CAR GARAGE 24-1x12-6

KITCHEN

W.I.C

MUD ROOM LAUNDRY

ENTRY

OFFICE 15-9x12-1

2-CAR GARAGE 24-6x24-7

FRONT PORCH

First Floor
2,491 sq. ft.

© Copyright by designer/architect

BEDROOM FOUR 14-0x14-6

BEDROOM THREE 13-0x12-2

FAMILY ROOM 25-9x24-6

EXERCISE ROOM 20-7x13-7

UNFINISHED STORAGE/ MECHANICAL

UNFINISHED STORAGE

Optional Lower Level
1,584 sq. ft.

PLAN #904-155D-0143

Dimensions: 75'6" W x 63'10" D
Heated Sq. Ft.: 2,269
Bonus Sq. Ft.: 456
Bedrooms: 3   Bathrooms: 2½
Foundation: Crawl space or slab standard; basement or daylight basement for an additional fee
See index on page 104 for more information

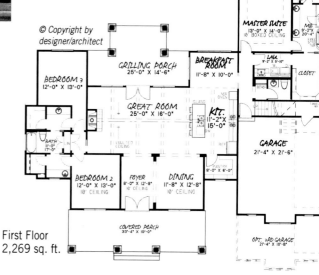

© Copyright by designer/architect

Optional Second Floor 456 sq. ft.

BONUS ROOM 23'-4" X 17'-0"

First Floor 2,269 sq. ft.

PLAN #904-152D-0049

Dimensions: 95' W x 48' D
Heated Sq. Ft.: 1,527
Bedrooms: 2   Bathrooms: 2
Exterior Walls: 2" x 6"
Foundation: Slab
See index on page 104 for more information

© Copyright by designer/architect

First Floor 1,032 sq. ft.

Second Floor 495 sq. ft.

PLAN #904-051D-0977

Dimensions: 58' W x 64'4" D
Heated Sq. Ft.: 1,837
Bedrooms: 3   Bathrooms: 2
Exterior Walls: 2" x 6"
Foundation: Basement standard;
crawl space or slab for an additional
fee

See index on page 104 for more information

© Copyright by
designer/architect

Second Floor
1,370 sq. ft.

PLAN #904-032D-1123

Dimensions: 44' W x 46'6" D
Heated Sq. Ft.: 2,496
Bonus Sq. Ft.: 1,126
Bedrooms: 4   Bathrooms: 2½
Foundation: Basement standard;
crawl space, monolithic slab or
floating slab for an additional fee

See index on page 104 for more information

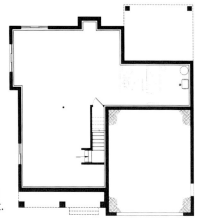

Optional
Lower Level
1,126 sq. ft.

First Floor
1,126 sq. ft.

© Copyright by
designer/architect

PLAN #904-167D-0009

Dimensions: 67'11" W x 65'10" D
Heated Sq. Ft.:   3,363
Bedrooms: 4   Bathrooms: 3½
Exterior Walls: 2" x 6"
Foundation: Crawl space standard;
slab for an additional fee
See index on page 104 for more information

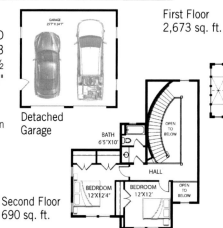

Detached
Garage

© Copyright by
designer/architect

First Floor
2,673 sq. ft.

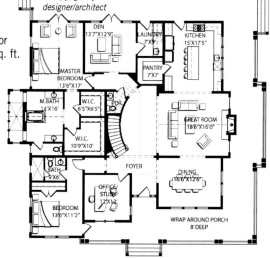

DEN
13'7"X12'9"

LAUNDRY
7'X9'

KITCHEN
15'X17'5"

MASTER
BEDROOM
13'6"X17'

PANTRY
7'X7'

M.BATH
14'X16'

W.I.C.
6'5"X6'5"

PDR.

GREAT ROOM
18'6"X16'0"

W.I.C.
10'9"X10'

FOYER

DINING
16'6"X12'6"

BATH
9'X6'

BEDROOM
13'5"X11'2"

OFFICE/
STUDY
12'X12'

WRAP AROUND PORCH
8' DEEP

BATH
6'5"X10'

OPEN
TO
BELOW

HALL

OPEN
TO
BELOW

BEDRROOM
12'X12'4"

BEDROOM
12'X12'

Second Floor
690 sq. ft.

PLAN #904-087D-1682

Dimensions: 25' W x 32' D
Heated Sq. Ft.:   740
Bedrooms: 1   Bathrooms: 1
Foundation: Slab
See index on page 104 for more information

© Copyright by designer/architect

BEDROOM
10 x 10

CLO.
4 x 3

BATH
5 x 10

LAUNDRY

HALL

CTS.

KITCHEN
8 x 15

UP

LIVING AREA
16 x 11

PAN.

First Floor
592 sq. ft.

"VAULTED"
PORCH
21 x 5

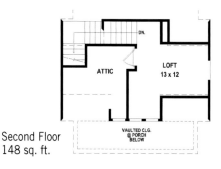

DN.

ATTIC

LOFT
13 x 12

VAULTED CLG.
@ PORCH
BELOW

Second Floor
148 sq. ft.

CALL 1-800-373-2646   ONLINE houseplansandmore.com

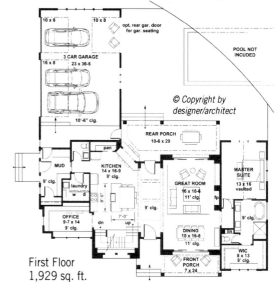

PLAN #904-091D-0518

Dimensions: 67' W x 75'2" D
Heated Sq. Ft.: 3,011
Bedrooms: 4   Bathrooms: 3½
Exterior Walls: 2" x 6"
Foundation: Basement standard;
daylight basement for an additional
fee
See index on page 104 for more information

Second Floor
1,082 sq. ft.

© Copyright by
designer/architect

First Floor
1,929 sq. ft.

PLAN #904-028D-0103

Dimensions: 40' W x 46' D
Heated Sq. Ft.: 1,520
Bedrooms: 2   Bathrooms: 1
Exterior Walls: 2" x 6"
Foundation: Crawl Space
See index on page 104 for more information

© Copyright by
designer/architect

Images provided by designer/architect

PLAN #904-155D-0131

Dimensions: 108'2" W x 92'4" D
Heated Sq. Ft.: 4,140
Bedrooms: 5   Bathrooms: 5½
Foundation: Crawl space or slab
standard; basement or daylight
basement for an additional fee
See index on page 104 for more information

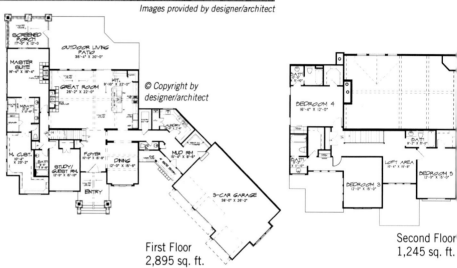

© Copyright by
designer/architect

First Floor
2,895 sq. ft.

Second Floor
1,245 sq. ft.

PLAN #904-026D-2091

Images provided by designer/architect

Dimensions: 42' W x 51'4" D
Heated Sq. Ft.: 1,603
Bedrooms: 3   Bathrooms: 2
Foundation: Basement standard;
crawl space, slab or walk-out
basement for an additional fee
See index on page 104 for more information

© Copyright by
designer/architect

PLAN #904-155D-0148

Dimensions:	72'6" W x 64'8" D
Heated Sq. Ft.:	1,897
Bonus Sq. Ft.:	395
Bedrooms: 4	Bathrooms: 2

Foundation: Crawl space or slab standard; basement or daylight basement for an additional fee

See index on page 104 for more information

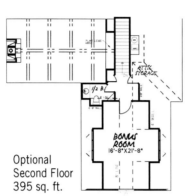

Optional
Second Floor
395 sq. ft.

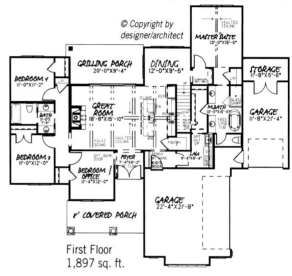

© Copyright by designer/architect

First Floor
1,897 sq. ft.

PLAN #904-026D-2011

Dimensions:	40' W x 50'8" D
Heated Sq. Ft.:	1,750
Bedrooms: 3	Bathrooms: 2½
Exterior Walls:	2" x 6"

Foundation: Basement standard; crawl space, slab or walk-out basement for an additional fee

See index on page 104 for more information

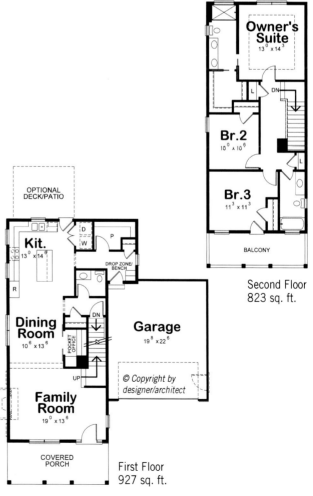

Second Floor
823 sq. ft.

First Floor
927 sq. ft.

PLAN #904-091D-0529

Dimensions: 68'4" W x 76'2" D
Heated Sq. Ft.: 2,570
Bonus Sq. Ft.: 440
Bedrooms: 3   Bathrooms: 3½
Exterior Walls: 2" x 6"
Foundation: Basement standard;
slab, crawl space or walk-out
basement for an additional fee
See index on page 104 for more information

Second Floor
715 sq. ft.

First Floor
1,855 sq. ft.

PLAN #904-026D-2013

Dimensions: 57'8" W x 58' D
Heated Sq. Ft.: 1,925
Bedrooms: 3   Bathrooms: 2
Exterior Walls: 2" x 6"
Foundation: Basement standard;
crawl space, slab or walk-out
basement for an additional fee
See index on page 104 for more information

CALL 1-800-373-2646   **ONLINE** houseplansandmore.com

PLAN #904-139D-0079

Dimensions:	99' W x 35' D
Heated Sq. Ft.:	3,830
Bonus Sq. Ft.:	800
Bedrooms: 4	Bathrooms: 3½
Exterior Walls:	2" x 6"

Foundation: Crawl space standard; slab, basement, daylight basement or walk-out basement for an additional fee

See index on page 104 for more information

© Copyright by designer/architect

First Floor
2,923 sq. ft.

Second Floor
907 sq. ft.

PLAN #904-051D-0815

Dimensions:	65' W x 49' D
Heated Sq. Ft.:	2,510
Bedrooms: 3	Bathrooms: 2½
Exterior Walls:	2" x 6"

Foundation: Basement standard; crawl space or slab for an additional fee

See index on page 104 for more information

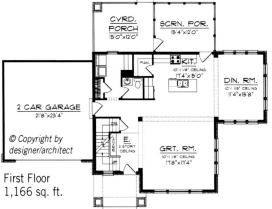

© Copyright by designer/architect

First Floor
1,166 sq. ft.

Second Floor
1,344 sq. ft.

HOME PLAN INDEX

PLEASE NOTE: Plan pricing is subject to change without notice. For current pricing, visit houseplansandmore.com, or call us at 1-800-373-2646.

Plan Number	Square Feet	PDF File	5-Sets	CAD File	Material List	Page
904-007D-5060	1,344	$889	$889	$1,389	-	85
904-011D-0579	2,292	$1,377	$1,552	$2,754	$220	12
904-011D-0617	2,104	$1,201	$1,351	$2,402	$170	53
904-011D-0622	2,490	$1,467	$1,642	$2,934	$220	78
904-011D-0627	1,878	$1,256	$1,431	$2,512	$170	55
904-011D-0630	2,495	$1,450	$1,625	$2,900	$170	30
904-011D-0646	2,292	$1,437	$1,612	$2,874	$220	19
904-011D-0650	2,213	$1,499	$1,674	$2,998	$170	39
904-011D-0652	2,448	$1,429	$1,604	$2,858	$220	15
904-011D-0653	3,032	$1,634	$1,809	$3,268	$220	59
904-011D-0657	1,394	$1,068	$1,243	$2,136	$220	43
904-011D-0658	2,618	$1,490	$1,665	$2,980	$220	63
904-011D-0660	1,704	$1,213	$1,388	$2,426	$170	84
904-011D-0661	2,508	$1,472	$1,647	$2,944	$170	31
904-011D-0662	2,460	$1,453	$1,628	$2,906	$170	34
904-011S-0196	7,149	$2,967	$3,142	$5,934	$220	56
904-020D-0386	2,754	$1,050	$1,130	$2,100	-	15
904-024S-0024	3,610	$3,025	-	$3,025	-	13
904-026D-1913	3,322	$1,115	-	$1,951	-	72
904-026D-1942	2,509	$935	-	$1,636	-	14
904-026D-2011	1,750	$955	-	$1,671	$125	101
904-026D-2013	1,925	$975	-	$1,706	-	102
904-026D-2079	1,600	$945	-	$1,654	-	19
904-026D-2091	1,603	$945	-	$1,654	-	100
904-026D-2092	2,448	$1,025	-	$1,794	-	91
904-026D-2094	1,822	$965	-	$1,689	-	52
904-028D-0097	1,908	$870	$970	-	-	16
904-028D-0099	1,320	$745	$870	-	-	82
904-028D-0100	1,311	$745	$870	-	$75	90
904-028D-0103	1,520	$870	$970	-	-	99
904-028D-0104	2,160	$995	$1,070	-	-	31
904-028D-0108	890	$695	$770	-	-	42
904-028D-0113	2,582	$1,020	$1,170	-	-	32
904-032D-0865	1,587	$1,020	$970	$1,700	$150	54
904-032D-0877	1,283	$1,020	$970	$1,700	$150	46
904-032D-0887	1,212	$950	$900	$1,630	$140	35
904-032D-0935	1,050	$870	$830	$1,560	$130	42
904-032D-0963	1,178	$870	$830	$1,560	$130	44
904-032D-0971	1,212	$1,020	$970	$1,700	$150	79
904-032D-1034	3,164	$1,260	$1,280	$2,010	$185	74
904-032D-1067	3,599	$1,450	$1,420	$2,150	$195	21
904-032D-1069	3,532	$1,450	$1,420	$2,150	$195	29
904-032D-1078	3,497	$1,350	$1,350	$2,080	$190	38
904-032D-1104	1,920	$1,080	$1,040	$1,770	$160	77
904-032D-1123	2,496	$1,140	$1,130	$1,860	$170	97
904-032D-1124	2,117	$1,080	$1,040	$1,770	$160	11
904-051D-0815	2,510	$1,316	$1,046	$2,091	-	103
904-051D-0960	2,784	$1,352	$1,081	$2,162	-	40
904-051D-0962	3,205	$1,397	$1,112	$2,224	-	26
904-051D-0977	1,837	$1,188	$949	$1,887	-	97
904-051D-0978	1,871	$1,188	$949	$1,887	-	74
904-051D-0979	1,921	$1,188	$949	$1,887	-	30
904-051D-0980	1,958	$1,188	$949	$1,887	-	58
904-052D-0157	2,067	$989	$989	$1,589	-	21
904-052D-0170	3,290	$1,289	$1,289	$2,189	-	10
904-052D-0171	3,562	$1,289	$1,289	$2,189	-	67
904-055D-0990	2,555	$2,050	$2,150	$4,100	-	41
904-055S-0115	4,501	$2,050	$2,150	$4,100	-	17
904-056D-0096	2,510	$2,295	-	$3,245	-	11
904-056D-0104	1,925	$1,245	-	$2,095	-	94
904-056D-0131	3,154	$1,245	-	$2,095	-	64
904-076D-0220	3,061	$1,950	$1,200	$2,600	-	76
904-077D-0019	1,400	$1,300	$1,200	$1,725	$150	91
904-077D-0288	2,107	$1,465	$1,365	$1,990	$150	34
904-077D-0293	1,800	$1,465	$1,365	$1,990	$150	78
904-084D-0082	1,599	$1,050	$1,090	$1,950	-	47
904-084D-0085	2,252	$1,150	$1,190	$2,100	-	45
904-087D-1682	740	$1,010	$830	$1,090	-	98
904-091D-0508	2,528	$2,040	$1,719	$2,723	-	29
904-091D-0509	2,886	$2,040	$1,719	$2,723	-	27
904-091D-0518	3,011	$2,040	$1,719	$2,723	-	99
904-091D-0523	2,514	$2,040	$1,719	$2,723	-	62
904-091D-0524	2,480	$2,040	$1,719	$2,723	-	20
904-091D-0529	2,570	$2,040	$1,719	$2,723	-	102
904-101D-0050	4,784	$3,050	-	$4,300	-	92
904-101D-0056	2,593	$1,400	-	$2,650	-	10
904-101D-0062	2,648	$1,400	-	$2,650	-	61
904-101D-0065	2,269	$1,250	-	$2,350	-	73
904-101D-0067	2,726	$1,600	-	$2,900	-	66
904-101D-0068	3,231	$1,850	-	$3,350	-	84
904-101D-0076	2,491	$1,400	-	$2,650	-	95
904-101D-0080	2,682	$1,400	-	$2,650	-	36
904-101D-0087	3,880	$1,950	-	$3,550	-	83
904-101D-0088	2,442	$1,400	-	$2,650	-	93
904-101D-0090	2,875	$1,600	-	$2,900	-	59
904-101D-0093	2,615	$1,400	-	$2,650	-	8
904-101D-0094	2,650	$1,400	-	$2,650	-	80
904-111D-0042	1,074	$995	$1,095	$1,995	-	18
904-121D-0011	2,241	$1,089	$1,089	$1,789	$125	43
904-121D-0025	1,368	$889	$889	$1,389	$125	47
904-121D-0039	1,624	$989	$989	$1,589	-	79
904-130D-0387	1,878	$1,005	-	$1,300	-	53
904-130D-0389	2,137	$1,025	-	$1,320	-	75
904-139D-0059	2,775	$1,495	$1,620	$2,995	-	95
904-139D-0061	3,210	$1,495	$1,620	$2,995	-	26
904-139D-0068	3,274	$1,495	$1,620	$2,995	-	52
904-139D-0079	3,830	$1,495	$1,620	$2,995	-	103
904-139D-0086	4,357	$1,495	$1,620	$2,995	-	63
904-139D-0087	3,409	$1,495	$1,620	$2,995	-	58
904-139D-0088	3,121	$1,495	$1,620	$2,995	-	28
904-139D-0089	3,734	$1,495	$1,620	$2,995	-	38
904-139D-0091	3,163	$1,495	$1,620	$2,995	-	46
904-139D-0092	2,966	$1,495	$1,620	$2,995	-	55
904-139D-0094	2,915	$1,495	$1,620	$2,995	-	75
904-139D-0097	2,715	$1,495	$1,620	$2,995	-	66
904-141D-0202	5,317	$2,244	$2,281	$2,931	-	62
904-141D-0223	2,095	$1,219	$1,256	$1,906	-	54
904-144D-0023	928	$1,040	$880	$1,440	$95	35
904-144D-0024	1,024	$1,040	$880	$1,440	$95	20
904-152D-0049	1,527	$1,907	-	$1,907	-	96
904-155D-0070	2,464	$1,550	$1,650	$3,100	-	37
904-155D-0110	2,711	$1,550	$1,650	$3,100	-	94
904-155D-0118	3,310	$2,650	$2,750	$5,300	-	39
904-155D-0128	2,687	$1,650	$1,750	$3,300	-	65
904-155D-0129	2,220	$1,350	$1,450	$2,700	-	28
904-155D-0131	4,140	$1,850	$1,950	$3,700	-	100
904-155D-0143	2,269	$1,100	$1,200	$2,200	-	96
905-155D-0147	2,073	$1,350	$1,450	$2,700	-	27
904-155D-0148	1,897	$1,200	$1,300	$2,400	-	101
904-157D-0022	3,820	$1,060	$1,160	$2,120	-	14
904-157D-0023	2,873	$1,029	$1,134	$2,058	-	90
904-167D-0003	2,569	$1,189	$1,189	$1,989	-	18
904-167D-0006	2,939	$1,189	$1,189	$1,989	-	85
904-167D-0008	3,328	$1,289	$1,289	$2,189	-	60
904-167D-0009	3,363	$1,289	$1,289	$2,189	-	98
904-170D-0003	2,672	$945	$995	$1,795	-	67